Praise for Jonathan Ba Research and Program

"I am often asked when there will be a proven prescription for weight loss. This is that prescription."
- **Harvard Medical School's** Dr. Theodoros Kelesidis

"A treasure trove of reliable information...hot, hot hot!"
- **Harvard Medical School's** Dr. JoAnne Manson

"Reveals the real story of diet, exercise, and their effects on us. I heartily recommend this." - **Harvard Medical School's** Dr. John J. Ratey

"Opens the black box of fat loss and makes it simple!"
- **Dr. Oz's Personal Trainer** Joel Harper

"I'm a big fan" – **World's Top Trainer and Creator of P90X** Tony Horton

"Will do more to assist people with their health than all the diet books out there put together. I want to shout, 'Bravo! Finally someone gets it!'"
- Dr. Christiane Northrup, **New York Times best-selling author** of *Women's Bodies, Women's Wisdom* and *The Wisdom of Menopause*

"Provides a powerful set of tools for creating lifelong health!"
- Dr. Mark Hyman, **New York Times best-selling author** of *The Blood Sugar Solution* and *The Daniel Plan*

"An easily understood and applied framework that will change the way you live, look, and feel... will end your confusion once and for all."
- Dr. William Davis, **New York Times best-selling author** of *Wheat Belly*

"Cuts through the noise around weight loss and tells it to us straight."
- Dr. Sara Gottfried, **New York Times best-selling author** of *The Hormone Cure* and *The Hormone Reset Diet*

"Readers will find that focusing on the kinds of foods they are eating can boost their brain power and help them lose the extra ten pounds."
- Dr. Daniel G. Amen, **New York Times best-selling author** of *Change Your Brain, Change Your Body*

"Will change the way you look at dieting!"
- JJ Virgin, **New York Times best-selling author** of *The Virgin Diet*

See hundreds more medical reviews and success stories at:
www.SANESolution.com

To my best friend, partner, and wife, Angela. Just the thought of you brings me more joy, more satisfaction, and more life than anything else I have ever experienced. You are my beloved, without reservation or qualification, as we dance into eternity.

To my heroes and parents, Mary Rose and Robert. All that I am is thanks to your love, example, and support. From the day I was born, and every day after, you have always found a way to help and love me. I live, hoping to return the favor.

To my friends and partners, Scott, Tyler, Sean, Abhishek, April, Lori, Wednesday, Josh, Jason, Andrea, and Rebecca, my delightful sister Patty, my wonderful brothers Tim, Cameron, and Branden, and my loving in-laws Terry and Carolyn. You are such treasures. Thank you for being who you are and thank you for meaning so much to me.

To you and the hundreds of thousands of other SANE family members all around the world with the courage to eat and exercise smarter. You have taken the road less traveled and it will make all the difference.

Published in the Worldwide by Yopti, LLC (SANESolution) New York. Seattle. California. www.SANESolution.com.

SANE books can be purchased at quantity discounts to use as premiums, promotions, or for corporate training programs. For more information on bulk pricing please email Yopti, LLC at SANESolution.com/contact.

Editor: Mary Rose Bailor
Production: Abhishek Pandey
Exterior Design: Tyler Archer

Publisher's Cataloging-in-Publication
Bailor, Jonathan.
99 Calorie Myth and SANE Certified Breakfast, Lunch, and Soup Recipes: Lose Weight, Increase Energy, Improve Your Mood, Fix Digestion, and Sleep Soundly With The Delicious New Science of SANE Eating/ Jonathan Bailor.—1st ed.
p. cm.
1. Health   2. Weight Loss   3. Cooking   4. Recipes   5. Diet   6. Nutrition
I. Bailor, Jonathan II. Title.

Manufactured in the United States of America. First Edition.

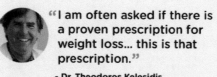

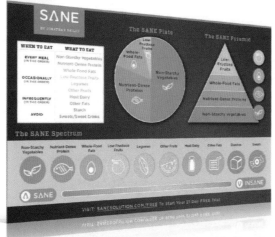

TABLE OF CONTENTS

TIP: Not familiar with the SANE Food Group or SANE Serving Sizes?

It's all good! Get everything you need by attending your FREE masterclass at SANESeminar.com and by downloading your FREE tools at SANESolution.com/Tools.

INTRODUCTION

Welcome to the SANE family! Jonathan Bailor here and I want to thank you again for taking time out of your hectic schedule to ensure that **your dinner table is for savoring and smiles, not self-criticism and calorie math**. Eating should be a source of joy and wellness, not shame and sickness. I sincerely hope that our time together will open your eyes to how easy it can be to reach your weight and fitness goals once you break free from the confusing and conflicting outdated theories and lies that have trapped you for so long.

If you only take one thing away from this book let it be this: **Any weight problem you may be experiencing is not your fault!** I know that may sound trite, but it's true. How can you be expected to lose those annoying pounds when all you've been given is outdated science and methods from the 1960's that have been proven NOT to work.

My mission is to not only reshape your body, but it's also to reshape the way you think about weight loss. What that means is I will be here with you every step of the way to provide all the support and tools you need to finally reach your weight loss goals. Whether you need to lose a few extra pounds around your belly, are looking for a **complete body transformation**, want **all-day energy**, or just want to make sense of all the confusing and conflicting health information out there once and for all, you are **finally in the right place!**

> TIP: Be sure to add service@SANESolution.com to your email safe senders list/address book. This ensures you get all your upcoming SANE bonus recipes, tools, and how-to videos.

So if you are ready to stop counting calories... Ready to stop killing yourself with exercise you hate... Ready to end your struggle with weight... and are tired of being hungry and tired...this is your chance. It's time to get off the dieting roller-coaster once and for all. **Are you ready?**

I urge you to make a commitment to yourself to continue this journey. You are worth it. After all, you took action to get this book so that means you are ready and willing to step up and make positive changes. If you follow the simple and scientifically backed principles we teach, **I promise you will lose weight...and keep it off for good.**

You are part of the family now, and I am so excited to have you here as we bust the myths that have been holding you back... perhaps for years. Remember this...**now is your time**, and these are your proven tools for lasting weight loss success. Welcome home.

Can't wait to meet you at
SANESolution.com,

Jonathan Bailor
New York Times Bestselling Author,
SANE Founder, and soon...your
personal weight-loss coach

P.S. Over the years I have found that our most successful members, the ones who have lost 60, 70, even 100 pounds...and kept it off...are the ones who started their personal weight-loss plan on our FREE half-day Masterclass. It's your best opportunity to fall in love with the SANE lifestyle, learn exactly how to start making the simple changes that lead to dramatic body transformations, and get introduced to your new SANE family. **Be sure to reserve your spot now at http://SANESeminar.com.**

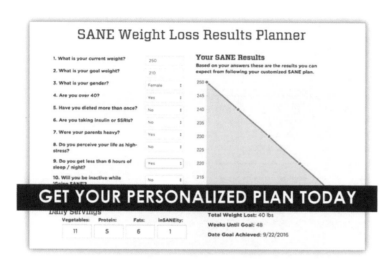

Breakfast

ASPARAGUS FRITTATA

Total Time: 50 min
Prep: 20 min
Cook: 30 min

6 Servings
1 Non-Starchy Vegetable Per Serving
1 Nutrient-Dense Protein Per Serving
1 Whole-Food Fat Per Serving

Ingredients

- 6 eggs + 24 egg whites
- 1/3 cup milk
- 1/4 teaspoon salt
- 1/8 teaspoon ground black pepper
- 1/2 cup Swiss cheese

- 1 teaspoon butter
- 3 cups sliced mushrooms
- 1/4 cup chopped shallots or ¼ cup red onion
- 24 fresh asparagus spears, cut into 2-inch lengths (or green beans)

Directions

1. Preheat broiler.

2. Beat eggs, milk, salt and pepper in a medium-size bowl until blended.

3. Stir in ½ cup cheese. Set aside.

4. Melt butter in a 10-inch nonstick skillet with ovenproof handle over medium heat. Add mushrooms, shallots and asparagus (or green beans). Cook and stir 3 minutes until vegetables are crisp, yet tender.

5. Reduce heat to medium and pour egg mixture over vegetables. Cover and cook 10 minutes, or until bottom of frittata is set, carefully lifting edge with spatula and tilting skillet as necessary to allow uncooked portion to flow underneath.

6. Place skillet under broiler. Broil 2 minutes or until top is set but not brown.

7. Top with remaining ½ cup cheese. Let stand until cheese has melted.

8. Cut into 6 wedges.

Asparagus Scrambled Eggs

Total Time: 15 min
Prep: 5 min
Cook: 10 min

4 Servings
2 Non-Starchy Vegetable Per Serving
1 Nutrient-Dense Protein Per Serving
1 Whole-Food Fat Per Serving

Ingredients

- 2 lbs asparagus, trimmed of tough ends
- 4 eggs + 16 egg whites
- 1 tablespoon basil leaves, minced
- 1 teaspoon butter

- 2 ounces neufchatel cheese, cut into 1/2 in pieces
- 1/4 cup shredded mozzarella cheese
- 3 tablespoons grated parmesan cheese
- salt and pepper

Directions

1. Bring one inch of water to a boil in a large saucepan. Meanwhile cut asparagus into one inch pieces.

2. Add asparagus to boiling water and cook until barely tender, 2-3 minutes.

3. Drain and set aside.

4. Beat eggs, salt and pepper to taste and the basil until well blended.

5. Heat a large non stick skillet.

6. Add butter and spread to cover skillet.

7. Add the eggs; sprinkle with the neufchatel cheese. As the egg sets, use a large spatula to softly scramble eggs. When eggs are still a little runny, add the asparagus, the mozzarella and parmesan. Keep on scrambling eggs until set to your taste.

8. Serve garnished with more basil, if desired.

BABY SPINACH OMELET

Total Time: 9 min
Prep: 2 min
Cook: 7 min

2 Servings
1 Non-Starchy Vegetable Per Serving
1 Nutrient-Dense Protein Per Serving
1 Whole-Food Fat Per Serving

Ingredients

- 4 eggs & 8 egg whites
- 6 cups Baby Spinach, torn
- 3 tablespoons parmesan cheese, grated

- 1/2 teaspoon onion powder
- 1/8 teaspoon ground nutmeg
- salt and pepper

Directions

1. In a bowl, beat the eggs, and stir in the baby spinach and Parmesan cheese. Season with onion powder, nutmeg, salt, and pepper.

2. In a small skillet coated with cooking spray over medium heat, cook the egg mixture about 3 minutes, until partially set. Flip with a spatula, and continue cooking 2 to 3 minutes.

3. Reduce heat to low, and continue cooking 2 to 3 minutes, or to desired doneness.

BAKED EGGS

Total Time: 45 min
Prep: 10 min
Cook: 35 min

4 Servings
1 Non-Starchy Vegetable Per Serving
1 Whole-Food Fat Per Serving

Ingredients

- 1 tablespoon extra virgin coconut oil
- 1 garlic clove, finely chopped
- 1/2 cup tomatoes (fresh, diced)

- kosher salt and pepper
- 20 ounces baby spinach leaves
- 8 eggs, separated (yolks kept whole, if possible)

Directions

1. Heat oven to 400°F.

2. Heat the oil in a medium skillet over medium-high heat. Add the garlic and cook for 1 minute. Add the tomatoes, 1/2 teaspoon salt, and 1/4 teaspoon pepper and simmer for 5 minutes. Add the spinach and cook until it begins to wilt, 1 minute. Transfer to a 2-quart baking dish.

3. Beat the egg whites until foamy, about 30 seconds, then pour them over the spinach mixture. Carefully place the whole yolks over the top.

4. Bake until the whites are set, 20 to 22 minutes. Divide among individual plates.

BAKED MINI FRITTATAS

Total Time: 25 min
Prep: 15 min
Cook: 10 min

8 Servings
1 Nutrient-Dense Protein Per Serving
1 Whole-Food Fat Per Serving

Ingredients

- 8 eggs & 12 egg whites
- 1/2 cup coconut milk
- 1/2 teaspoon black pepper
- 1/4 teaspoon salt

- 4 ounces ham, chopped
- 1/3 cup parmesan cheese, grated
- 2 tablespoons Italian parsley, chopped

Directions

1. Preheat the oven to 375 degrees.

2. Spray 2 mini muffin tins (each with 24 cups) with nonstick spray.

3. Whisk the eggs, milk, pepper, and salt in a large bowl to blend well.

4. Stir in the ham, cheese, and parsley.

5. Fill prepared muffin cups almost to the top with the egg mixture.

6. Bake until the egg mixture puffs and is just set in the center, about 10 to 15 minutes.

7. Using a rubber spatula, loosen the frittatas from the muffin cups and slide the frittatas onto a platter.

Blue Mushroom Omelet

Total Time: 25 min
Prep: 15 min
Cook: 10 min

2 Servings
1 Non-Starchy Vegetable Per Serving
1 Nutrient-Dense Protein Per Serving
1 Whole-Food Fat Per Serving

Ingredients

- 4 eggs + 8 egg whites
- 1 tablespoon whole milk
- 4 pinches ground black pepper
- 2 pinches garlic salt, or to taste
- 2 teaspoons extra virgin coconut oil

- 4 cremini mushrooms, sliced
- 2 tablespoons chopped red onion
- 4 cups baby spinach, coarsely chopped
- 1/2 ounce crumbled Stilton cheese
- 1/2 cup shredded part-skim mozzarella cheese

Directions

1. Lightly whisk the eggs with the milk in a bowl to break the yolks and integrate the milk; season with 4 pinches black pepper and 2 pinches garlic salt.

2. Heat extra virgin coconut oil in a non-stick skillet over medium heat; cook and stir mushrooms and onion in hot oil until the onion softens, about 5 minutes.

3. Spread the mushrooms and onion into the bottom of the skillet so it forms an even layer.

4. Sprinkle wilted spinach evenly across the top of the mushroom and onion layer.

5. Pour egg mixture over the vegetables.

6. Cook until the top of the egg is set, 3 to 5 minutes.

7. Sprinkle Stilton cheese and mozzarella cheese over the cooked egg; cook until the mozzarella begins to melt, fold the omelet in half around the filling to make a half-moon.

BREAKFAST LOAF

Total Time: 1hr 30 min
Prep: 30 min
Cook: 1hr

8 Servings
1 Non-Starchy Vegetable Per Serving
1 Nutrient-Dense Protein Per Serving
1 Whole-Food Fat Per Serving

Ingredients

- 1 pound ground turkey
- 1 cup powdered milk
- 3 eggs, beaten
- 1 green bell peppers, chopped
- 1/2 small onion, chopped

- 2 stalks celery, chopped
- 10 oz package frozen spinach, thawed and drained
- 1/2 teaspoon ground black pepper
- 1/2 teaspoon ground sage

Directions

1. Preheat oven to 350 degrees F (175 degrees C). Lightly grease an 8×11 inch baking dish.
2. In a large bowl, mix together the ground turkey, powdered milk, and eggs until well blended.
3. Mix in the green peppers, onion, celery and spinach.
4. Season with black pepper and sage.
5. Press the mixture into the prepared pan.
6. Bake for 1 hour in the preheated oven, or until the center is firm and the juices run clear.
7. Let stand for a few minutes before slicing into 16 slices.

CHEESE OMELET

Total Time: 6 min
Prep: 2 min
Cook: 4 min

1 Serving
1 Non-Starchy Vegetable Per Serving
1 Nutrient-Dense Protein Per Serving
1 Whole-Food Fat Per Serving

Ingredients

- 2 eggs + 6 egg whites
- 1/2 tablespoon milk
- 3 pinches salt

- 3 pinches pepper
- Coconut oil
- ¼ cup Swiss cheese

Directions

1. Preheat omelet pan on medium heat.

2. Mix eggs, milk, salt, and pepper until frothy. (Don't over whisk).

3. Put ½ tsp coconut oil in heated pan so omelet does not stick.

4. Pour mixture into pan and wait till it is cooked and thick. If it falls apart in pan, let it cook more.

5. Next, when the omelet is thick and does not fall apart when lifted take put ¼ cup shredded cheese on one side of omelet.

6. Flip the uncheesed side of omelet to the side of the omelet with cheese. Wait until cheese melts and take off and into plate.

Cocotte Eggs

Total Time: 7 min
Prep: 2 min
Cook: 5 min

2 Servings
1 Nutrient-Dense Protein Per Serving
1 Whole-Food Fat Per Serving

Ingredients

- 2 teaspoons blue cheese, crumbled
- 2 eggs + 8 egg whites
- 2 teaspoons creme fraiche

- 2 pinches chives, chopped
- salt
- pepper

Directions

1. Heat the oven to 375ºF/190ºC.
2. Into the bottom of each of two buttered ramekins put a spoonful of blue cheese
3. Gently crack an egg in on top & gently add 4 egg whites
4. Top with a spoonful of crème fraîche.
5. Season with salt and pepper.
6. Sprinkle over the chives.
7. Set the ramekins in a baking dish and pour hot water in the dish to come half-way up the sides of the ramekins.
8. Bake until cooked, but still jiggling, 5 to 7 minutes.

DELUXE OMELET

Total Time: 10 min
Prep: 5 min
Cook: 5 min

1 Serving
1 Non-Starchy Vegetable Per Serving
1 Nutrient-Dense Protein Per Serving
1 Whole-Food Fat Per Serving

Ingredients

- 2 eggs + 4 egg whites
- 1 tablespoon milk
- 1/3 cup ham, diced
- 1 cup chopped red bell pepper
- chopped scallion
- 1/8 teaspoon garlic powder
- salt and pepper
- coconut oil cooking spray

Directions

1. Spray pan with coconut oil cooking spray.

2. Scramble eggs and add milk.

3. Combine with remaining ingredients and pour into pan.

4. Cook as you would any omelet.

DELUXE OMELET IN A BAG

Total Time: 15 min
Prep: 5 min
Cook: 10 min

2 Servings
1 Non-Starchy Vegetable Per Serving
1 Nutrient-Dense Protein Per Serving
1 Whole-Food Fat Per Serving

Ingredients

- 4 eggs + 8 egg whites
- salt & freshly ground black pepper
- ¼ cup shredded mozzarella cheese
- 1 cup diced onion
- 1 cup diced bell pepper (green, red, yellow)
- 1 cup diced tomato
- 1 cup diced ham
- 1 cup sliced mushrooms
- 1/3 cup sliced black olives
- 2 cups chopped spinach

Directions

1. Bring a large pot of water to a boil.

2. In a large bowl, whisk together half of all ingredients.

3. Seal each baggie tight.

4. Combine with hands to combine the egg mixture.

5. Drop each sealed baggie into the boiling water.

6. Simmer the bags for 8 to 10 minutes or until done to your desire.

7. Remove baggies from boiling water with tongs and drain on a paper towel lined plate or strainer.

8. Cool slightly before handing.

9. Open baggie and pour the cooked omelet onto each individual plate.

EASY CUP 'O OMELET

Total Time: 8 min
Prep: 5 min
Cook: 3 min

1 Serving
1 Nutrient-Dense Protein Per Serving
1 Whole-Food Fat Per Serving
1 Non-Starchy Vegetable Per Serving

Ingredients

- 1 egg & 6 egg whites
- 1 teaspoon onion, finely minced
- 1 mushroom, chopped

- 1/2 cup wilted spinach
- 1 tablespoon parmesan cheese
- pepper, to taste

Directions

1. Mix all in very large mug and microwave for 3 mins.

Egg Muffins

Total Time: 12 min
Prep: 2 min
Cook: 10 min

4 Servings
1 Nutrient-Dense Protein Per Serving
1 Whole-Food Fat Per Serving

Ingredients

- 4 eggs + 12 egg whites
- 2 tablespoons milk
- 1 tablespoon fresh parsley, chopped

- 1/3 cup parmesan cheese
- 3 slices cooked bacon, chopped

Directions

1. Beat eggs in a medium bowl.

2. Add remaining ingredients.

3. Grease a mini muffin tin.

4. Fill cups with egg mixture until almost to the rim.

5. Bake at 375 degrees for 10-15 minutes or until centers are set.

FRENCH HERB OMELET

Total Time: 15 min
Prep: 5 min
Cook: 10 min

4 Servings
1 Non-Starchy Vegetable Per Serving
1 Nutrient-Dense Protein Per Serving
1 Whole-Food Fat Per Serving

Ingredients

- 6 eggs & 16 egg whites
- 1/2 teaspoon fresh ground black pepper
- 1/4 teaspoon salt
- 1/4 cup parsley
- 1/8 cup tarragon
- 1/8 cup chives
- 2 teaspoons extra virgin coconut oil

Directions

1. Beat the eggs, pepper and salt in a bowl.

2. Stir in the herbs.

3. Heat 1 teaspoon each of the oil in a nonstick frying pan over high heat.

4. When the oil is hot, add half the egg mixture.

5. Stir it continuously with a fork while shaking the pan for about 2 minutes to create small curds.

6. When most of the mixture is solid, cook it without stirring for 10 seconds to create a thin skin on the underside of the mixture, binding it together.

7. Roll the omelet by bringing together 2 opposite edges.

8. Invert in a plate.

9. Repeat process using remainder of ingredients to create a second omelet.

10. Serve immediately, half an omelet per person.

FRITTATA RICOTTA

Total Time: 30 min
Prep: 10 min
Cook: 20 min

6 Servings
1 Nutrient-Dense Protein Per Serving
1 Whole-Food Fat Per Serving

Ingredients

- 6 eggs + 16 egg whites
- 1 cup ricotta cheese
- 1/4 cup freshly grated parmesan cheese
- 1 1/2 tablespoons chopped marjoram

- 1 clove garlic, crushed
- 1 tablespoon extra virgin coconut oil
- salt
- white pepper

Directions

1. Preheat broiler Beat eggs with ¾ teaspoon salt and white pepper to taste.
2. Stir in cheeses, marjoram and garlic.
3. Heat oil in 8- or 10-inch skillet.
4. Add egg mixture and lower heat.
5. Cook until set, about 12 minutes, then brown under broiler.
6. When done, slide frittata onto plate.

Gold Rush Eggs

Total Time: 20 min
Prep: 5 min
Cook: 15 min

4 Servings
1 Nutrient-Dense Protein Per Serving
1 Whole-Food Fat Per Serving

Ingredients

- 1 tsp butter
- 3 eggs + 12 egg whites
- 1/3 cup milk
- 1 medium tomato, chopped

- 2 tablespoons chopped chives
- 1/4 teaspoon salt
- 1 dash pepper
- 2 ounces any white cheese, cubed

Directions

1. Melt butter in skillet over low heat.

2. Add combined eggs, milk, tomato and seasonings.

3. Cook slowly stirring only occasionally until eggs are set.

4. Add process cheese spread and cook until cheese begins to melt.

Greek Eggs

Total Time: 10 min
Prep: 5 min
Cook: 5 min

1 Serving
1 Nutrient-Dense Protein Per Serving
1 Whole-Food Fat Per Serving

Ingredients

- 1 tsp coconut oil
- 2 eggs + 4 egg whites
- 1/4 cup crumbled feta cheese
- salt and pepper (optional)

Directions

1. Heat oil in a skillet over medium-high heat.

2. Beat eggs, then pour into pan.

3. Add feta cheese, and cook, stirring occasionally to scramble.

4. Season with salt and pepper.

.

GREEK OMELET

Total Time: 15 min
Prep: 5 min
Cook: 10 min

2 Servings
1 Non-Starchy Vegetable Per Serving
1 Nutrient-Dense Protein Per Serving
1 Whole-Food Fat Per Serving

Ingredients

- 4 eggs + 8 egg whites
- 1/4 cup feta cheese
- 6 cups fresh spinach

- oregano
- salt & pepper

Directions

1. Spray a skillet with nonstick cooking spray.
2. Place spinach into skillet and cook on medium heat until spinach begins to shrivel.
3. Set spinach aside.
4. Beat eggs together and pour into warm skillet.
5. Sprinkle feta cheese and precooked spinach over top.
6. Sprinkle with oregano, salt, and pepper.
7. After eggs appear to be cooked 1/2 way through, fold omelet in half and cook until center reaches desired consistency.

.

GREEK SCRAMBLE

Total Time: 25 min
Prep: 10 min
Cook: 15 min

2 Servings
2 Non-Starchy Vegetable Per Serving
1 Nutrient-Dense Protein Per Serving
1 Whole-Food Fat Per Serving

Ingredients

- 2 cups bell pepper, finely sliced (green or red)
- 2 garlic cloves, chopped
- 1/4 cup yellow onion, finely sliced
- 1 teaspoon extra virgin coconut oil
- 2 cups zucchini, sliced into bite sized pieces (or squash of your choice)

- 1/2 cup fresh tomato, diced
- 3 eggs + 10 egg whites
- 2 tablespoons pitted kalamata olives, sliced
- crumbled feta cheese, to taste
- salt & pepper, To taste

Directions

1. Warm extra virgin coconut oil in frying pan over medium heat.

2. Once sizzling hot (I test by dropping small amount of water into oil) put onions, garlic and bell peppers into pan, sauté until lightly browned.

3. Add zucchini and cook until zucchini is slightly softened but still firm.

4. Mix in tomatoes and olives.

5. Add eggs, salt and pepper to taste, then cook until eggs are no longer "wet".

6. Remove from pan and sprinkle with Feta to taste.

HAM AND CHEESE SCRAMBLE

Total Time: 10 min
Prep: 5 min
Cook: 5 min

2 Servings
1 Nutrient-Dense Protein Per Serving
1 Whole-Food Fat Per Serving

Ingredients

- 2 eggs + 10 egg whites
- 1 tablespoon milk

- 1 cup cubed ham
- 1/2 cup shredded Cheddar cheese

Directions

1. Preheat a skillet over medium heat.

2. Combine eggs and milk in a large bowl; beat well.

3. Add ham to preheated skillet and warm until juicy.

4. Add eggs and stir regularly until they start to set.

5. While eggs are still soft, add cheese.

6. Cook until eggs are firm and cheese is melted.

7. Season with salt and pepper to taste and serve.

HAM AND EGG BAKE

Total Time: 1hr 15 min
Prep: 20 min
Cook: 55 min

6 Servings
1 Non-Starchy Vegetable Per Serving
1 Nutrient-Dense Protein Per Serving
1 Whole-Food Fat Per Serving

Ingredients

- cooking spray
- 8 eggs + 16 egg whites
- 1/2 cup skim milk
- 1/2 cup low-fat sour cream
- 1/2 teaspoon salt
- 3 cups chopped cooked ham
- 6 cups chopped red bell pepper
- 6 cups sliced fresh mushrooms
- 1 cup sliced green onion
- 1/2 cup shredded Cheddar cheese

Directions

1. Preheat oven to 325 degrees F (165 degrees C). Prepare a 13×9-inch baking dish with cooking spray.

2. Beat eggs, milk, sour cream, and salt together in a large bowl with wire whisk until well blended.

3. Mix ham, bell peppers, mushrooms, and green onion into the egg mixture; pour into the prepared baking dish.

4. Bake in the preheated oven until a knife inserted into the center comes out clean, about 50 minutes.

5. Cover top of dish with Cheddar cheese; continue baking until cheese is melted, about 3 minutes.

.

Ham Frittata

Total Time: 45 min
Prep: 10 min
Cook: 35 min

4 Servings
1 Non-Starchy Vegetable Per Serving
1 Nutrient-Dense Protein Per Serving
1 Whole-Food Fat Per Serving

Ingredients

- 1 tablespoon extra virgin coconut oil
- 1 cup cooked ham, cubed
- 1/2 cup onion, chopped
- 3 cups red sweet bell pepper, chopped
- 3 cups green bell pepper, chopped
- 1 cup celery, chopped
- 2 jalapeno peppers, seeded and chopped
- 2 tablespoons jalapeno jelly, at room temperature (optional)
- 4 eggs + 16 egg whites
- 1/4 teaspoon salt
- 1/2 teaspoon cracked black pepper or 1/2 teaspoon red pepper flakes
- 1/4 cup cheddar cheese, grated

Directions

1. Heat oven to 400°F.

2. Heat oil in a non stick frypan, add ham cubes and onions.

3. Sauté until onions are transparent and just turning brown, about 5 to 7 minutes.

4. Add red, green and jalapeño peppers, celery and jalapeño jelly, if using.

5. Sauté 3 to 5 minutes or until jelly melts.

6. In a large bowl, beat eggs with salt and pepper, until frothy and about double in volume.

7. Over high heat pour egg mixture evenly over evenly spread sautéed mixture.

8. Move mixture around just a little.

9. Place lid on frypan and leave on high heat until bottom is set, being careful not to burn.

10. Do not remove lid.

11. Place covered frypan on middle rack in oven and cook approximately 20 minutes, until well risen and golden (I have a see-through lid on my frypan).

12. Remove lid and sprinkle with cheddar cheese, turn oven to broil, broil for 2 or 3 minutes until cheddar melts.

13. Slide onto platter and cut into 4 pieces, serve hot with salsa if desired.

INSTANT OMELET

Total Time: 3 min
Prep: 2 min
Cook: 1 min

1 Serving
1 Non-Starchy Vegetable Per Serving
1 Nutrient-Dense Protein Per Serving
1 Whole-Food Fat Per Serving

Ingredients

- 1 egg + 4 egg whites
- 1 tablespoon water
- 1 tablespoon chopped sweet onion
- 1/2 cup chopped white mushroom

- 1/2 cup chopped bell peppers
- 1 TBSP shredded sharp cheddar cheese
- 1 teaspoon chopped tomato, as garnish if desired
- coconut oil cooking spray

Directions

1. Spray small glass custard cup with coconut oil spray.
2. Put eggs into cup and beat with fork until yolk and white are mixed.
3. Add water and mix.
4. Chop vegetables (meat) into very small pieces and mix with egg in custard cup.
5. Add shredded cheese-mix lightly.
6. Season to taste.
7. Put custard cup on a microwave safe plate and place in microwave oven on high for 1 ½ minutes or until cooked through.
8. Carefully remove and invert custard cup onto plate. Add garnish as desired.

.

ITALIAN EGGS

Total Time: 10 min
Prep: 5 min
Cook: 5 min

2 Servings
1 Nutrient-Dense Protein Per Serving
1 Whole-Food Fat Per Serving

Ingredients

- 1 tomato
- extra virgin coconut oil
- chopped fresh basil or chopped fresh pesto sauce

- salt
- white pepper
- 2 eggs + 8 egg whites
- 1 TSP coconut oil
- 2 basil leaves

Directions

1. Cut the top of the tomato off.

2. Gently squeeze the tomato to remove juice with the seeds, then chop in small pieces.

3. Sauté tomato for a couple of minutes in olive oil and fresh basil (or pesto) add salt and pepper.

4. Add eggs and coconut oil to the skillet and scramble.

5. Divide egg mixture between 2 plates, garnish with a basil leave.

.

Kale Frittata

Total Time: 45 min
Prep: 15 min
Cook: 30 min

4 Servings
2 Non-Starchy Vegetable Per Serving
1 Nutrient-Dense Protein Per Serving
1 Whole-Food Fat Per Serving

Ingredients

- 6 large eggs + 12 egg whites
- 3/4 tsp kosher salt
- 1/2 tsp black pepper
- 3 tbsps Parmesan cheese
- 2 tbsp chopped oregano

- Cooking spray
- 4 cups Braised Kale, drained, finely chopped
- 1 cup chopped cherry tomatoes

Directions

1. Preheat oven to 375°F. In a large bowl, whisk the first 6 ingredients (through oregano).

2. Lightly coat an 8-inch ovenproof cast-iron or nonstick skillet with cooking spray. Heat over medium.

3. Add the braised kale and tomatoes. Cook, stirring, until hot (about 3 minutes). Add the eggs and swirl to distribute.

4. Transfer to the oven and bake until set and hot (about 20 minutes). Cut in wedges.

MEXICAN OMELET

Total Time: 10 min
Prep: 3 min
Cook: 7 min

1 Serving
1 Nutrient-Dense Protein Per Serving
1 Whole-Food Fat Per Serving

Ingredients

- 2 eggs + 4egg whites
- 1 TBSP cheddar cheese
- 1/2 tsp coconut oil

- Taco seasoning to taste
- Salt
- Pepper

Directions

1. Scramble eggs in a bowl.

2. Melt oil in a pan.

3. Add your eggs and when it looks like the edges are starting to set add your cheese and taco seasoning.

4. Gently fold your omelet and flip.

MINI FRITTATAS

Total Time: 25 min
Prep: 15 min
Cook: 10 min

6 Servings
1 Nutrient-Dense Protein Per Serving
1 Whole-Food Fat Per Serving

Ingredients

- 6 large eggs + 16 egg whites
- 1/2 cup skim milk
- 1/2 teaspoon fresh ground black pepper
- 1/4 teaspoon salt
- 4 ounces thinly sliced ham, chopped
- 1/3 cup freshly grated parmesan cheese
- 2 tablespoons chopped fresh Italian parsley

Directions

1. Preheat oven to 375 degrees.
2. Spray two mini non-stick muffin tins (each with 24 cups) with nonstick spray.
3. Fill prepared cups almost to the tops with egg mixture.
4. Bake until eggs puff and are just set in center, about 8-10 minutes.
5. Using a rubber spatula, loosen frittatas from the cups and slide onto a platter.
6. Serve immediately or at room temperature.

MINI OMELET CUPS

Total Time: 50 min
Prep: 30 min
Cook: 20 min

2 Servings
1 Whole-Food Fat Per Serving

Ingredients

- 4 eggs
- salt and pepper
- Your choice of diced veggies

Directions

1. Preheat your oven to 350 degrees. Coat a six cup muffin pan with nonstick cooking spray.

2. Whisk together the eggs, half and half and salt in a medium bowl, then evenly distribute the egg mixture among the muffin cups.

3. Add about 2 tablespoons of diced veggies mix ins to each cup.

4. Bake the omelets until they are puffy and the edges are golden brown, about 20 – 25 minutes.

5. If necessary run a butter knife around the edge of each one of the omelets to loosen them before removing them from the pan.

MUSHROOM AND PEPPER FRITTATA

Total Time: 45 min
Prep: 15 min
Cook: 30 min

10 Servings
1 Non-Starchy Vegetable Per Serving
1 Nutrient-Dense Protein Per Serving
1 Whole-Food Fat Per Serving

Ingredients

- 1 tablespoon extra virgin coconut oil
- 1 thinly sliced onion
- 5 thinly sliced green bell peppers
- 5 cups sliced mushrooms
- 1 garlic clove, minced
- 6 large eggs + 24 egg whites

- 1/3 cup 1% low-fat milk
- 3/4 teaspoon salt
- 1/4 teaspoon black pepper
- 1 tablespoon chopped fresh or 1 teaspoon dried basil
- 1 tablespoon butter
- 1 cup cherry tomatoes, halved
- 1/2 cup fontina cheese, cut into small cubes

Directions

1. Heat oil in a 10-inch, oven-safe skillet or sauté pan. Add onion and pepper; sauté over medium heat 5 minutes, stirring frequently. Add mushrooms, cover, and sauté 3 minutes, stirring several times. Add garlic, and sauté 1 additional minute. Remove vegetable mixture from heat, and transfer to a plate to cool briefly. Wipe pan with paper towels, and return to stove.

2. Combine eggs, egg whites, milk, salt, pepper, and basil in a large bowl, stirring with a whisk until well blended; set aside. Heat skillet over medium heat for 2-3 minutes and add butter, swirling pan to melt butter evenly. Add vegetables to egg mixture in bowl, stir, and carefully pour entire mixture into heated skillet. Scatter cherry tomatoes and cheese over egg mixture (do not stir).

3. Cook frittata gently over medium-low heat 15-18 minutes or until it is cooked most of the way through. To finish cooking the top, preheat broiler and place the frittata about 6-8 inches from heat for 2-4 minutes (watch frittata carefully to ensure that it doesn't burn).

4. Remove frittata from oven, cool on a wire rack for 5 minutes, and shake pan rapidly back and forth to loosen. Cool a few more minutes, then carefully put a plate over the frittata and invert it onto the plate. Invert it again onto another plate so the frittata is right side up. Refrigerate until ready to serve.

MUSHROOM OMELET

Total Time: 5 min
Prep: 3 min
Cook: 2 min

1 Serving
1 Non-Starchy Vegetable Per Serving
1 Nutrient-Dense Protein Per Serving
1 Whole-Food Fat Per Serving

Ingredients

- 2 eggs + 4 egg whites
- salt and pepper (or freshly cracked peppercorn)
- 1 pinch garlic powder

- 1 pinch tarragon
- 2 pinches sweet basil
- 1 cup sliced mushrooms

Directions

1. Set burner to medium to medium high (depending on your preference).

2. Whisk eggs in a small bowl.

3. Whisk in remaining ingredients.

4. If burner is on medium, pour the eggs onto the pan first.

5. If burner is on medium high, whisk in mushrooms before pouring onto pan.

6. Flip omelet constantly so mushrooms don't burn.

7. Use your judgement as to when the omelet is ready. My omelet took a little under 2 minutes on medium high.

Easy Quiche

Total Time: 45 min
Prep: 10 min
Cook: 35 min

6 Servings
1 Non-Starchy Vegetable Per Serving
1 Nutrient-Dense Protein Per Serving
1 Whole-Food Fat Per Serving

Ingredients

- 6 eggs + 16 egg whites
- 3 cups broccoli, chopped
- 3 cups mushroom, chopped
- 1/4 cup cheddar cheese, grated
- 1/4 cup bacon, cooked and chopped
- 1/2 teaspoon salt
- 1/4 teaspoon pepper
- 1/4 teaspoon thyme

Directions

1. Preheat oven to 350 degrees.

2. Spray a 9″ pie pan with cooking spray.

3. Mix ingredients.

4. Pour into prepared pie pan.

5. Bake for 35 minutes.

OMELET 2.0

Total Time: 3 min
Prep: 1 min
Cook: 2 min

2 Servings
1 Non-Starchy Vegetable Per Serving
1 Nutrient-Dense Protein Per Serving
1 Whole-Food Fat Per Serving

Ingredients

- 2 eggs + 10 egg whites
- 1/2 teaspoon garlic salt
- 2 tablespoons chicken broth
- 2 tablespoons grated mozzarella cheese
- cooking spray
- 2 cups mushrooms

Directions

1. Slice up mushrooms

2. Heat the pan with cooking spray.

3. Beat eggs, garlic salt and chicken broth together and pour in hot pan.

4. Sprinkle cheese on top.

5. Make sure both sides of omelet are cooked.

6. Serve.

OMELET SOUFFLÉ

Total Time: 20 min
Prep: 10 min
Cook: 10 min

4 Servings
1 Non-Starchy Vegetable Per Serving
1 Nutrient-Dense Protein Per Serving
1 Whole-Food Fat Per Serving

Ingredients

- 4 eggs + 16 egg whites
- 1 pinch salt and pepper
- 2 teaspoons fresh parsley, chopped
- 2 tablespoons cream

- 1 tablespoon butter
- 2 tablespoons brie cheese, roughly chopped
- 2 cups sautéed mushroom
- 2 cups sautéed onion

Directions

1. Beat egg yolks until thick and light in color.

2. Add cream, salt, pepper, and parsley.

3. Beat egg whites till they form peaks then fold into yolk mixture and gentle toss in mushrooms and onions.

4. Pour into a hot buttered cast iron pan.

5. Cook slowly until omelet puffs up and is firm on the bottom.

6. Place into a preheated oven 350 degrees for about 3 minutes then sprinkle brie on top and bake for 2 more minutes.

7. Fold omelet in half and serve.

ONION AND BACON OMELET

Total Time: 35 min
Prep: 15 min
Cook: 20 min

2 Servings
1 Nutrient-Dense Protein Per Serving
1 Whole-Food Fat Per Serving

Ingredients

- 2 strips bacon
- 1 teaspoon butter
- 1/2 sweet onion, diced
- 2 eggs + 10 egg whites
- 2 tablespoons water

- 1/4 cup shredded sharp Cheddar cheese
- 1/8 teaspoon salt
- 1/8 teaspoon crushed red pepper flakes

Directions

1. Cook bacon in a skillet over medium-high heat until crisp. Remove with a slotted spoon to paper towels to drain and cool; crumble the bacon and set aside.

2. Melt the butter in a skillet over medium heat. Cook and stir the onions in the butter until tender, about 10 minutes.

3. Prepare a 10-inch non-stick skillet with cooking spray and place over a cold burner.

4. Whisk together the eggs and water; pour the egg mixture into the cold skillet. Cover and turn the burner on for medium-low heat. Cook until steam begins to vent from the skillet. Remove the lid.

5. Sprinkle the crumbled bacon, Cheddar cheese, salt, and red pepper over the eggs. Spread the onions over the eggs. Gently swirl the skillet in a circular motion to release the omelet and slide it onto a plate.

6. Fold the omelet in half. Allow the cheese to melt, about 2 minutes.

PHILLY SCRAMBLE

Total Time: 20 min
Prep: 5 min
Cook: 15 min

4 Servings
1 Nutrient-Dense Protein Per Serving
1 Whole-Food Fat Per Serving

Ingredients

- 2 tsp coconut oil
- 4 eggs + 16 egg whites
- 1/3 cup milk

- 3 ounces cream cheese
- Salt & pepper, to taste

Directions

1. Melt butter in skillet on low heat.
2. Add eggs, milk, seasoning.
3. Cook slowly stirring until eggs start to thicken.
4. Add cream cheese.
5. Cook, stirring occasionally until cheese melts.

Quick Egg White Omelet

Total Time: 20 min
Prep: 10 min
Cook: 10 min

4 Servings
2 Non-Starchy Vegetable Per Serving
1 Nutrient-Dense Protein Per Serving

Ingredients

- cooking spray
- 1 cup chopped onion
- 4 cups chopped green bell pepper
- 4 cups chopped mushrooms
- salt and pepper to taste
- 20 egg whites
- 2 cups cooked spinach

Directions

1. Spray a 9×5-inch glass or microwave-safe loaf pan with cooking spray; sprinkle the onion, green bell pepper, spinach, and mushrooms into the pan, and toss lightly with a fork just to mix.

2. Season with salt and black pepper, and pour in the egg whites.

3. Cook in a microwave oven on High setting for 3 minutes.

4. Remove and stir the cooked egg white from the side of the pan into the rest of the ingredients; cook for 3 more minutes on High.

5. If the omelet is still a little runny on top, slice it into chunks and turn them over in the loaf pan; microwave for 30 more seconds on High.

6. Adjust salt and pepper, and serve.

.

SAUSAGE FRITTATA

Total Time: 45 min
Prep: 15 min
Cook: 30 min

6 Servings
1 Nutrient-Dense Protein Per Serving
1 Whole-Food Fat Per Serving

Ingredients

- 14 oz Turkey Sausage, halved lengthwise, and cut into 1/4-inch-thick slices
- 1 cup diced green onions, white and green parts
- 1 tablespoons extra virgin coconut oil
- 6 eggs + 20 egg whites
- 1/3 cup shredded mozzarella cheese

- 1/3 cup freshly grated Parmesan cheese
- 16 torn fresh basil leaves
- 1/4 cup chopped sun-dried tomatoes
- 1/4 teaspoon ground black pepper
- Freshly grated Parmesan cheese (optional)
- Fresh basil leaves (optional)

Directions

1. Preheat oven to 350 degrees F.

2. Cook and stir sausage and onions in extra virgin coconut oil in heavy oven-proof 10-inch skillet on medium heat 5 minutes or until light golden brown.

3. Combine remaining ingredients in medium bowl. Stir egg mixture into skillet mixture. Cook on medium heat, lifting with a rubber spatula once or twice, to allow uncooked portion to flow underneath. Cook just until egg mixture begins to set, about 6 minutes.

4. Place skillet in oven. Bake 5 to 7 minutes or until egg mixture is firm to the touch and top is golden brown.

5. Remove skillet from oven. Carefully run a spatula around edge of frittata to loosen from skillet. Invert skillet onto serving platter. Cut frittata into quarters. Garnish each portion with Parmesan cheese and basil, if desired.

SCRAMBLED EGG MUFFINS

Total Time: 40 min
Prep: 20 min
Cook: 20 min

4 Servings
1 Non-Starchy Vegetable Per Serving
1 Nutrient-Dense Protein Per Serving
1 Whole-Food Fat Per Serving

Ingredients

- 1 1/2 cup chopped ham
- 4 eggs + 16 egg whites
- 1/2 cup chopped onion
- 4 cups chopped green pepper

- 1/2 teaspoon hot pepper sauce
- 1/4 teaspoon salt
- 1/8 teaspoon pepper
- 1/8 teaspoon garlic powder
- 1/4 cup shredded sharp cheddar cheese

Directions

1. Preheat oven to 350°F.

2. Brown ham; drain well.

3. In a bowl mix eggs with onion, green peppers, salt, pepper and garlic powder.

4. Stir in ham and cheese.

5. Spoon 1/3 cupfuls into greased muffin cups.

6. Bake at 350°F for 20-25 minutes or until a knife inserted comes out clean.

SKILLET SCRAMBLE

Total Time: 15 min
Prep: 10 min
Cook: 5 min

1 Serving
1 Nutrient-Dense Protein Per Serving
1 Whole-Food Fat Per Serving

Ingredients

- 2 eggs + 4 egg whites
- 3 tablespoons milk
- 1/8 cup salt

- 1 dash ground pepper
- 1 teaspoon butter
- 1/4 teaspoon minced garlic

Directions

1. In a medium bowl beat together eggs, milk, salt, and pepper with a wire whisk or fork.
2. In a 6 ½ inch skillet melt butter over med heat; add garlic and cook until soft. Pour in egg mixture.
3. Cook over med heat, without stirring, until mixture begins to set on the bottom and around edge.
4. With a spatula or a large spoon, lift and fold the partially cooked egg mixture so that the uncooked portion flows underneath.
5. Continue cooking over med heat for 2 to 3 minutes or until egg mixture is cooked through but is still glossy and moist.
6. Remove from heat and serve.

SPINACH AND SAUSAGE BAKE

Total Time: 1hr
Prep: 20 min
Cook: 40 min

8 Servings
1 Non-Starchy Vegetable Per Serving
1 Nutrient-Dense Protein Per Serving
1 Whole-Food Fat Per Serving

Ingredients

- 1 pound Italian sausage
- 1 (8 ounce) can all-natural tomato sauce
- 3 (10 ounce) packages frozen chopped spinach, thawed and drained

- 2 cups low-fat cottage cheese
- 1/4 cup grated Parmesan cheese
- 6 egg whites
- 1 cup shredded mozzarella cheese

Directions

1. Brown sausage in skillet over medium high heat. Drain fat from skillet and stir in tomato sauce. Set mixture aside.

2. Preheat oven to 350 degrees F (175 degrees C).

3. In a large bowl, combine the spinach, cottage cheese, Parmesan cheese and egg.

4. Mix well and spread mixture in the bottom of a 9×13 inch baking dish.

5. Spoon sausage mixture over spinach mixture and top with mozzarella cheese.

6. Bake in preheated oven for 40 minutes.

.

TOMATO OMELET

Total Time: 20 min
Prep: 5 min
Cook: 15 min

1 Serving
1 Non-Starchy Vegetable Per Serving
1 Nutrient-Dense Protein Per Serving
1 Whole-Food Fat Per Serving

Ingredients

- 1 egg + 4 egg whites
- 2 tablespoons water
- 1 medium tomato, diced
- ground black pepper (to taste)
- 1 pinch parsley flakes
- 1 pinch allspice

Directions

1. Whisk eggs, water, pepper, and parsley flakes in a small bowl until frothy.

2. Pour mixture into a small pan and distribute tomatoes evenly over top.

3. Cook 10 minutes, or until edges are nice and crispy.

4. Season with allspice and serve.

Veggie Quiche Cups

Total Time: 40 min
Prep: 20 min
Cook: 20 min

6 Servings
1 Non-Starchy Vegetable Per Serving
1 Nutrient-Dense Protein Per Serving
1 Whole-Food Fat Per Serving

Ingredients

- 2 diced green bell peppers
- 2 diced red bell peppers
- 1 small diced onion
- 1 cup diced ham

- 2 cups diced mushroom
- 2 small tomatoes, diced
- 1/2 cup shredded sharp cheddar cheese
- 6 eggs + 16 egg whites
- salt and pepper

Directions

1. Preheat oven 350 degrees.

2. Spray muffin tins with extra virgin coconut oil.

3. Sauté veggies and ham

4. Mix eggs and shredded cheese

5. Place sautéed veggies and ham in bottom of each tin (approx. ½ tsp- depending on size of tins).

6. Pour egg and cheese mixture over each tin almost to top.

7. Bake 20 – 30 minutes again depends on size of tins.

8. Serve hot or cold.

.

ZESTY EGGS

Total Time: 20 min
Prep: 10 min
Cook: 10 min

2 Servings
1 Non-Starchy Vegetable Per Serving
1 Nutrient-Dense Protein Per Serving
1 Whole-Food Fat Per Serving

Ingredients

- 2 eggs + 8 egg whites
- 3 green onions, thinly sliced
- 4 pepperoni slices, diced
- 1/2 teaspoon garlic powder

- 1 teaspoon melted butter
- 1 TBSP grated Romano cheese
- 1 pinch salt and ground black pepper to taste
- 6 cups spinach

Directions

1. Wilt the spinach in a pan with water on medium heat

2. Whisk eggs, green onions, pepperoni slices, wilted spinach and garlic powder together in a bowl.

3. Heat butter in a non-stick skillet over low heat; add egg mixture, cover skillet, and cook until eggs are set, 10 to 15 minutes.

4. Sprinkle Romano cheese over eggs and season with salt and pepper.

.

LUNCH

TIP: Not familiar with the SANE Food Group or SANE Serving Sizes?

It's all good! Get everything you need by attending your FREE masterclass at SANESeminar.com and by downloading your FREE tools at SANESolution.com/Tools.

SPEEDY SALMON

Total Time: 15 min
Prep: 5 min
Cook: 10 min

8 Servings
2 Nutrient-Dense Protein Per Serving
1 Whole-Food Fat Per Serving

Ingredients

- 2 tablespoons garlic powder
- 2 tablespoons dried basil
- 1 teaspoon salt

- 8 (6 ounce) salmon
- 1/4 cup butter
- 8 lemon wedges

Directions

1. Stir together the garlic powder, basil, and salt in a small bowl; rub in equal amounts onto the salmon fillets.

2. Melt the butter in a skillet over medium heat; cook the salmon in the butter until browned and flaky, about 5 minutes per side. Serve each piece of salmon with a lemon wedge.

BREADED CATFISH

Total Time: 20 min
Prep: 10 min
Cook: 10 min

8 Servings
1 Nutrient-Dense Protein Per Serving
2 Whole-Food Fats Per Serving

Ingredients

- 2/3 cup almond flour
- 2 pinches salt and pepper to taste
- 8 (6 ounce) fillets catfish
- 1/4 cup extra virgin coconut oil
- 1/2 cup oyster sauce

Directions

1. In a bowl, mix the flour, salt, and pepper. Dredge the catfish fillets in the flour mixture to lightly coat.

2. Heat the extra virgin coconut oil in a large skillet over medium-high heat, and cook the catfish fillets 3 minutes on each side, until golden brown. Reduce heat to medium-low, and brush fillets with oyster sauce. Cover skillet, and continue cooking 5 minutes, or until fish is easily flaked with a fork.

SEA BASS CEVICHE

Total Time: 3hr 20 min
Prep: 20 min
Cook: 3hr

8 Servings
1 Nutrient-Dense Protein Per Serving
1 Whole-Food Fat Per Serving

Ingredients

- 2-3/4 TSP harissa
- 2/3 cup unsweetened coconut milk
- 2/3 cup fresh lemon juice
- 1/3 cup fresh lime juice
- 1/3 cup fresh orange juice
- 2-3/4 pounds Atlantic sea bass, diced
- 1/3 cup red onion, finely chopped
- 1-1/4 TSP minced ginger root

- 2 TBSP and 2 TSP extra virgin coconut oil
- 2 TBSP and 2 TSP chopped Moroccan preserved lemon
- 1 TBSP and 1 TSP caraway seed, lightly toasted and then crushed
- 3/4 TSP ground cumin
- 2 TBSP and 2 TSP chopped fresh chervil
- kosher salt to taste

Directions

1. In a large glass or ceramic bowl, whisk together the Harissa, coconut milk, lemon juice, lime juice and orange juice.

2. Add the sea bass, onion, ginger, melted extra virgin coconut oil, preserved lemon, caraway seed, cumin and chervil.

3. Stir to blend, then press everything down so there is a layer of liquid covering the top.

4. Cover and refrigerate for at least 3 hours, or until the fish is opaque and white. Season with salt and add more harissa if desired before serving.

SIMPLE ROUND ROAST

Total Time: 3hr 5 min
Prep: 5 min
Cook: 3hr

8 Servings
1 Nutrient-Dense Protein Per Serving
1 Whole-Food Fat Per Serving

Ingredients

- 1-1/4 (3 pound) beef eye of round roast

- salt and pepper to taste

Directions

1. Preheat the oven to 500 degrees F (260 degrees C). Season the roast with salt and pepper and place in a roasting pan or baking dish. Do not cover or add water.

2. Place the roast in the preheated oven. Reduce the temperature to 475 degrees F (245 degrees C). Roast for 21 minutes (seven minutes per pound) then turn off the oven and let the roast sit in the hot oven for 2 1/2 hours. Do not open the door at all during this time!

3. Remove the roast from the oven, the internal temperature should have reached at least 145 degrees F (65 degrees C). Carve into thin slices to serve.

OLD BAY TILAPIA

Total Time: 35 min
Prep: 5 min
Cook: 30 min

8 Servings
1 Nutrient-Dense Protein Per Serving
1 Whole-Food Fat Per Serving

Ingredients

- 8 (4 ounce) fillets tilapia
- 1 tablespoon and 1 teaspoon butter
- 1/2 teaspoon seafood seasoning

- 1 teaspoon garlic salt, or to taste
- 2 lemon, sliced
- 2 (16 ounce) packages frozen cauliflower with broccoli and red pepper

Directions

1. Preheat the oven to 375 degrees F (190 degrees F). Grease a 9×13 inch baking dish.

2. Place the tilapia fillets in the bottom of the baking dish and dot with butter. Season with seafood seasoning and garlic salt. Top each one with a slice or two of lemon. Arrange the frozen mixed vegetables around the fish, and season lightly with salt and pepper.

3. Cover the dish and bake for 25 to 30 minutes in the preheated oven, until vegetables are tender and fish flakes easily with a fork.

Easy Tri-Tip Roast

Total Time: 30 min
Prep: 5 min
Cook: 25 min

8 Servings
1 Nutrient-Dense Protein Per Serving
2 Whole-Food Fats Per Serving

Ingredients

- 1/4 cup garlic powder
- 2 tablespoons and 2 teaspoons salt
- 2 tablespoons and 2 teaspoons ground black pepper
- 2-3/4 pounds tri tip roast

Directions

1. Preheat an outdoor grill for high heat and lightly oil grate.

2. In a medium bowl, combine garlic powder, salt and pepper. Mix together and coat both sides of tri tip.

3. Sear both sides on hot grill then cook 20-25 minutes or until center is light pink. Slice at an angle.

Beautiful Baked Turkey Wings

Total Time: 2hr 10 min   8 Servings
Prep: 10 min   2 Nutrient-Dense Protein Per Serving
Cook: 2hr   1 Whole-Food Fat Per Serving

Ingredients

- 10 turkey wings
- 2 small onion, chopped (optional)
- 2 teaspoons seasoned salt
- 2 teaspoons poultry seasoning

- 2 teaspoons ground black pepper
- 2 teaspoons minced garlic
- 3 cups water, divided
- 2 (10.75 ounce) cans all-natural cream of mushroom soup

Directions

1. Preheat oven to 350 degrees F (175 degrees C).
2. Place turkey wings and onion in a casserole dish; sprinkle seasoned salt, poultry seasoning, black pepper, and garlic on both sides of each wing. Pour 1/2 cup water into the casserole dish. Cover casserole dish.
3. Bake in the preheated oven until browned, 1 hour.
4. Stir cream of mushroom soup and 1 cup water together in a bowl; pour over turkey wings into casserole dish and return to oven, uncovered.
5. Continue baking until brown and tender, 1 hour.

BEER BAKED PORK

Total Time: 2hr 40 min   6 Servings
Prep: 10 min   1 Nutrient-Dense Protein Per Serving
Cook: 2hr 30 min   2 Whole-Food Fats Per Serving

Ingredients

- 1 tablespoon and 1 teaspoon extra virgin coconut oil
- 4 pounds pork picnic roast

- 1-1/4 (12 fluid ounce) cans or bottles beer
- 1-1/4 large onion, sliced
- salt and ground black pepper to taste

Directions

1. Preheat oven to 350 degrees F (175 degrees C).

2. Heat oil in a Dutch oven or heavy pot over medium heat; cook pork in oil until evenly browned on all sides, about 15 minutes. Add beer.

3. Cover Dutch oven and bake in the preheated oven until pork is very tender, about 2 hours. Shred pork with a fork and transfer Dutch oven back to the stove top; stir in onion.

4. Cook and stir over medium heat until onion is browned, about 15 minutes. Season with salt and pepper.

Bourbon Pork

Total Time: 1hr
Prep: 15 min
Cook: 45 min

8 Servings
1 Nutrient-Dense Protein Per Serving
1 Whole-Food Fat Per Serving

Ingredients

- 1/4 cup soy sauce
- 1/4 cup bourbon
- 2 tablespoons xylitol
- 2 cloves garlic, halved
- 3 pounds pork tenderloin

Directions

1. Mix together soy sauce, bourbon, xylitol, and garlic. Pour over pork, cover, and refrigerate at least 2 hours, turning occasionally.

2. Preheat oven to 325 degrees F (165 degrees C). Remove pork from marinade, and place on rack of shallow roasting pan.

3. Bake for 45 minutes or until a meat thermometer registers 145 degrees F (63 degrees C).

CHICKEN AND SAUSAGE KABOBS

Total Time: 20 min
Prep: 10 min
Cook: 10 min

8 Servings
1 Nutrient-Dense Protein Per Serving
2 Whole-Food Fats Per Serving

Ingredients

- 4 skinless, boneless chicken breasts, cut into 20 pieces
- 1 pound chorizo sausage, cut into 16 pieces
- 2 tablespoons extra virgin coconut oil
- 2 tablespoons sherry vinegar
- 1 tablespoon and 1 teaspoon chopped fresh oregano
- 2 pinches cayenne pepper, or to taste
- salt and ground black pepper to taste
- 2 red onion, cut into 1-inch squares
- 2 red bell pepper, cut into 1-inch squares
- 8 (12-inch) bamboo skewers

Directions

1. Preheat an outdoor grill for medium-high heat and lightly oil the grate.

2. Place chicken and chorizo in a large bowl; add melted coconut oil, sherry vinegar, oregano, cayenne pepper, black pepper, and salt. Stir until chicken and chorizo are completely coated.

3. Thread chicken, chorizo, red onion, and red bell pepper evenly onto 4 skewers, making sure that each piece of chicken touches 1 piece of chorizo. Place finished skewers on a plate, cover with plastic wrap, and refrigerate until cold 15 to 30 minutes.

4. Cook on the preheated grill, turning occasionally, until chicken is cooked through, about 10 minutes.

CHICKEN PICCATA

Total Time: 25 min
Prep: 10 min
Cook: 15 min

8 Servings
1 Nutrient-Dense Protein Per Serving
2 Whole-Food Fats Per Serving

Ingredients

- 8 skinless, boneless chicken breast halves
- cayenne pepper, or to taste
- salt and ground black pepper to taste
- coconut flour for dredging
- 1/4 cup extra virgin coconut oil

- 2 tablespoons capers, drained
- 1 cup white wine
- 1/2 cup fresh lemon juice
- 1/2 cup water
- 1/4 cup and 2 tablespoons cold unsalted butter, cut in 1/4-inch slices
- 1/4 cup fresh Italian parsley, chopped

Directions

1. Place chicken breasts between 2 layers of plastic wrap and pound to about 1/2-inch thick.

2. Season both sides of chicken breasts with cayenne, salt, and black pepper; dredge lightly in flour and shake off any excess.

3. Heat extra virgin coconut oil in a skillet over medium-high heat. Place chicken in the pan, reduce heat to medium, and cook until browned and cooked through, about 5 minutes per side; remove to a plate.

4. Cook capers in reserved oil, smashing them lightly to release brine, until warmed though, about 30 seconds.

5. Pour white wine into skillet. Scrape any browned bits from the bottom of the pan with a wooden spoon. Cook until reduced by half, about 2 minutes.

6. Stir lemon juice, water, and butter into the reduced wine mixture; cook and stir continuously to form a thick sauce, about 2 minutes. Reduce heat to low and stir parsley through the sauce.

7. Return chicken breasts to the pan cook until heated through, 1 to 2 minutes. Serve with sauce spooned over the top.

CHICKEN STEW

Total Time: 55 min
Prep: 15 min
Cook: 40 min

8 Servings
2 Nutrient-Dense Protein Per Serving
2 Whole-Food Fats Per Serving

Ingredients

- 2 tablespoons and 2 teaspoons extra virgin coconut oil, divided
- 2 pounds skinless, boneless chicken breast halves – cut into 1 inch cubes
- 5/8 (12 ounce) jar roasted red bell peppers, drained
- 1-1/4 (14.5 ounce) cans diced tomatoes with juice
- 1-1/4 (6 ounce) jars mushrooms, drained
- 1-1/4 onion, diced
- 1 tablespoon and 1 teaspoon minced garlic
- salt and pepper to taste
- 1-1/4 (16 ounce) packages shredded mozzarella cheese

Directions

1. Preheat oven to 350 degrees F (175 degrees C). Lightly grease a medium casserole dish.

2. Heat 1 tablespoon oil in a skillet over medium heat, and cook the chicken until juices run clear.

3. Puree the roasted red peppers in a blender or food processor until smooth. In the prepared casserole dish, mix the cooked chicken, roasted red peppers, tomatoes, mushrooms, onion, and garlic. Season with salt and pepper. Drizzle with remaining 1 tablespoon olive oil, and top with mozzarella cheese.

4. Bake 30 minutes in the preheated oven, until cheese is melted and bubbly.

DELICATE TURKEY BREAST

Total Time: 50 min
Prep: 20 min
Cook: 30 min

8 Servings
1 Nutrient-Dense Protein Per Serving
2 Whole-Food Fats Per Serving

Ingredients

- 1-1/4 cloves garlic, peeled and minced
- 2 teaspoons finely chopped fresh basil
- 1/4 teaspoon ground black pepper
- 1-1/4 (3 pound) boneless turkey breast halves

- 4 whole cloves
- 2 tablespoons and 2 teaspoons extra virgin coconut oil
- 2 tablespoons and 2 teaspoons soy sauce
- 1 tablespoon and 1 teaspoon lemon juice
- 2 teaspoons brown sugar

Directions

1. In a small bowl, mix together the garlic, basil, and pepper. Rub over the turkey breasts. Insert one clove into each end of the turkey breasts, and one in the center.

2. In a large shallow dish, blend melted extra virgin coconut oil, soy sauce, lemon juice, and brown sugar. Place the breasts in the dish, and turn to coat. Cover, and marinate in the refrigerator at least 4 hours.

3. Preheat grill for high heat.

4. Lightly oil the grill grate. Discard marinade, place turkey breasts on the grill. Close the lid, and grill turkey breasts about 15 minutes on each side, or to an internal temperature of 170 degrees F (68 degrees C).

EASTERN CHICKEN KABOBS

Total Time: 40 min   8 Servings
Prep: 30 min   2 Nutrient-Dense Protein Per Serving
Cook: 10 min   2 Whole-Food Fats Per Serving

Ingredients

- 1/3 cup lemon juice
- 1/3 cup extra virgin coconut oil
- 1 cup plain yogurt
- 5-1/4 cloves garlic, minced
- 2-3/4 teaspoons tomato paste
- 2 teaspoons salt
- 1-1/4 teaspoons dried oregano
- 1/4 teaspoon ground black pepper
- 1/4 teaspoon ground allspice
- 1/4 teaspoon ground cinnamon
- 1/8 teaspoon ground cardamom
- 2-3/4 pounds skinless, boneless chicken breast halves – cut into 2 inch pieces
- 2-3/4 onions, cut into large chunks
- 1-1/4 large green bell pepper, cut into large chunks
- 1-1/3 cups chopped fresh flat-leaf parsley

Directions

1. Whisk together the lemon juice, coconut oil, plain yogurt, garlic, tomato paste, salt, oregano, pepper, allspice, cinnamon, and cardamom in a large bowl; add the chicken and toss to coat.

2. Transfer the chicken mixture into a large plastic bag; refrigerate at least 4 hours.

3. Preheat an outdoor grill for medium-high heat and lightly oil grate.

4. Thread the chicken, onions, and pepper onto metal skewers.

5. Cook on preheated grill until the chicken is golden and no longer pink in the center, about 5 minutes each side.

6. Sprinkle the parsley over the skewers.

Fiesta Beef

Total Time: 11hr 15 min   8 Servings
Prep: 15 min   1 Nutrient-Dense Protein Per Serving
Cook: 11hr   2 Whole-Food Fats Per Serving

Ingredients

- 4 pounds beef chuck roast, trimmed of fat and meat cut into chunks
- 1 (24 ounce) jar salsa
- 1 onion, chopped
- 1 (7 ounce) can chopped mild green chiles
- 2 cloves garlic, minced
- 2 teaspoons chili powder
- 1 1/2 teaspoons ground cumin
- 1/2 teaspoon dried oregano

Directions

1. Mix chuck roast, salsa, onion, green chile peppers, garlic, chili powder, cumin, and oregano in a slow cooker.

2. Cook on Low for 10 to 12 hours. Remove lid and cook on High for 1 more hour.

3. Remove chuck roast from slow cooker using a slotted spoon to a serving platter; shred meat with a fork.

4. Add liquid from slow cooker, 1 tablespoon at a time, to the chuck roast until desired consistency is reached.

FIESTA CHICKEN

Total Time: 45 min
Prep: 5 min
Cook: 40 min

8 Servings
2 Nutrient-Dense Protein Per Serving
1 Whole-Food Fat Per Serving
1 Most-Dairy Per Serving

Ingredients

- 8 skinless, boneless chicken breast halves
- 2 tablespoons and 2 teaspoons taco seasoning mix

- 2 cups salsa
- 2 cups shredded Cheddar cheese

Directions

1. Preheat oven to 375 degrees F (190 degrees C)

2. Place chicken breasts in a lightly greased 9×13 inch baking dish. Sprinkle taco seasoning on both sides of chicken breasts, and pour salsa over all.

3. Bake at 375 degrees F (190 degrees C) for 25 to 35 minutes, or until chicken is tender and juicy and its juices run clear.

4. Sprinkle chicken evenly with cheese, and continue baking for an additional 3 to 5 minutes, or until cheese is melted and bubbly.

Fiesta Cod

Total Time: 35 min
Prep: 5 min
Cook: 30 min

6 Servings
2 Nutrient-Dense Protein Per Serving
1 Whole-Food Fat Per Serving

Ingredients

- 3 pounds cod fillets
- 4 cups salsa

- 1/4 cup chopped fresh parsley
- salt and pepper to taste

Directions

1. Preheat oven to 350 degrees F (175 degrees C).

2. Rinse and dry cod fillets. Place fillets in a lightly greased casserole dish. Pour salsa over fish. Sprinkle with parsley, salt and pepper.

3. Bake in preheated oven for 30 minutes. Serve warm over rice.

FIESTA TURKEY

Total Time: 25 min   8 Servings
Prep: 10 min   2 Nutrient-Dense Protein Per Serving
Cook: 15 min   1 Whole-Food Fat Per Serving

Ingredients

- 2 teaspoons extra virgin coconut oil
- 2 onion, chopped
- 2 pounds shredded cooked turkey
- 2 teaspoons garlic powder
- 2 large fresh tomato, chopped
- 1 cup water
- 2 tablespoons chopped fresh cilantro
- salt and pepper to taste

Directions

1. Heat the oil in a skillet over medium heat, and cook the onion until tender.
2. Mix in turkey, and season with garlic powder.
3. Stir in the tomato.
4. Pour in water, sprinkle with cilantro, and season with salt and pepper.
5. Cover skillet, and simmer 5 minutes, or until heated through.

FRIED TURKEY WINGS

Total Time: 30 min
Prep: 5 min
Cook: 25 min

8 Servings
1 Nutrient-Dense Protein Per Serving
3 Whole-Food Fats Per Serving

Ingredients

- 8 turkey wings, cut apart at joints and wing tips discarded
- 1/4 cup seasoned salt
- 1 tablespoon and 1 teaspoon seafood seasoning (such as Old Bay®)

- 1 tablespoon and 1 teaspoon cayenne pepper
- 2 tablespoons and 2 teaspoons garlic powder
- 64 cups extra virgin coconut oil for deep frying

Directions

1. Season the turkey wing pieces on all sides with seasoned salt, seafood seasoning, cayenne pepper, and garlic powder. Place into a plastic bag, and refrigerate 4 hours to overnight.

2. Heat oil in a deep-fryer or large saucepan to 350 degrees F (175 degrees C).

3. Cook the turkey wings in the hot oil for 15 minutes, then turn the wings over, and continue cooking until the meat is no longer pink at the bone, 10 to 15 minutes.

Greek Salmon

Total Time: 40 min   8 Servings
Prep: 20 min   1 Nutrient-Dense Protein Per Serving
Cook: 20 min   2 Whole-Food Fats Per Serving

Ingredients

- 8 (5 ounce) salmon fillets, with skin
- 1/4 cup extra virgin coconut oil
- 4 plum tomatoes, diced
- 1/2 cup crumbled feta cheese
- 1/4 red onion, diced
- 1 tablespoon chopped fresh basil
- 4 kalamata olives, sliced
- 1 tablespoon lemon juice

Directions

1. Preheat an oven to 350 degrees F (175 degrees C).

2. Brush each salmon fillet on all sides with extra virgin coconut oil and arrange into the bottom of a glass baking dish with the skin side facing down. Scatter the tomatoes, feta cheese, onion, basil, and olives over the fillets; sprinkle with the lemon juice.

3. Bake in the preheated oven until the salmon flakes easily with a fork, about 20 minutes.

GRILLED PORK CHOPS

Total Time: 15 min
Prep: 5 min
Cook: 10 min

8 Servings
2 Nutrient-Dense Protein Per Serving
2 Whole-Food Fats Per Serving

Ingredients

- 2/3 cup water
- 1/4 cup and 3 tablespoons light soy sauce
- 1/3 cup extra virgin coconut oil

- 1/4 cup lemon pepper seasoning
- 2-3/4 teaspoons minced garlic
- 8 boneless pork loin chops, trimmed of fat

Directions

1. Mix water, soy sauce, extra virgin coconut oil, lemon pepper seasoning, and minced garlic in a deep bowl; add pork chops and marinate in refrigerator at least 2 hours.

2. Preheat an outdoor grill for medium-high heat and lightly oil the grate.

3. Remove pork chops from the marinade and shake off excess. Discard the remaining marinade.

4. Cook the pork chops on the preheated grill until no longer pink in the center, 5 to 6 minutes per side. An instant-read thermometer inserted into the center should read 145 degrees F (63 degrees C).

ITALIAN CHICKEN SKILLET

Total Time: 40 min
Prep: 20 min
Cook: 20 min

8 Servings
1 Nutrient-Dense Protein Per Serving
1 Whole-Food Fat Per Serving

Ingredients

- 1-1/2 cups chicken broth
- 3 tablespoons tomato paste
- 1/2 teaspoon ground black pepper
- 1 teaspoon dried oregano
- 1/4 teaspoon salt
- 2 cloves garlic, minced
- 8 boneless, skinless chicken breast halves
- 1/4 cup and 2 tablespoons dry bread crumbs
- 1 tablespoon and 1 teaspoon extra virgin coconut oil
- 4 cups fresh sliced mushrooms

Directions

1. In a medium bowl, combine the broth, tomato paste, ground black pepper, oregano, salt and garlic. Mix well and set aside.

2. Dredge the chicken in the bread crumbs, coating well. Heat the oil in a large skillet over medium high heat. Saute the chicken in the oil for 2 minutes per side, or until lightly browned.

3. Add the reserved broth mixture and the mushrooms to the skillet and bring to a boil. Then cover, reduce heat to low and simmer for 20 minutes. Remove chicken and set aside, covering to keep it warm.

4. Bring broth mixture to a boil and cook for 4 minutes, or until reduced to desired thickness. Spoon sauce over the chicken and serve.

Italian Herbed Chicken

Total Time: 20 min
Prep: 10 min
Cook: 10 min

8 Servings
1 Nutrient-Dense Protein Per Serving
1 Whole-Food Fat Per Serving

Ingredients

- 2 tablespoons and 2 teaspoons chopped Italian flat leaf parsley
- 2-3/4 teaspoons fresh rosemary, minced
- 2-3/4 teaspoons chopped fresh thyme
- 1-1/4 teaspoons dried sage
- 4 cloves garlic, minced
- 1/3 cup extra virgin coconut oil
- 2/3 cup balsamic vinegar
- salt and pepper to taste
- 2 pounds skinless, boneless chicken breasts

Directions

1. In a blender combine the parsley, rosemary, thyme, sage, garlic, extra virgin coconut oil, vinegar and salt and pepper to taste. Blend together. Place chicken in a nonporous glass dish or bowl and pour blended marinade over the chicken. Cover dish and refrigerate to marinate for at least 2 hours or up to 48 hours.

2. Preheat grill to medium high heat OR set oven to broil.

3. Remove chicken from dish (disposing of leftover marinade) and grill or broil for about 6 to 7 minutes per side, or until chicken is cooked through and no longer pink inside.

MEDITERRANEAN SALMON

Total Time: 30 min
Prep: 10 min
Cook: 20 min

8 Servings
1 Nutrient-Dense Protein Per Serving
3 Whole-Food Fats Per Serving

Ingredients

- 1 tablespoon and 1 teaspoon extra virgin coconut oil
- 8 (4 ounce) fillets salmon
- 1/2 cup extra virgin coconut oil

- 4 cloves garlic, minced
- 2 cups chopped tomatoes, or more to taste
- 1/4 cup balsamic vinegar
- 24 fresh basil leaves, chopped

Directions

1. Heat 1 teaspoon extra virgin coconut oil in a saucepan over medium heat. Cook salmon in the hot oil until cooked through and flakes easily with a fork, 5 to 7 minutes per side.

2. Heat 2 tablespoons extra virgin coconut oil in a separate saucepan over medium heat; add garlic and cook until fragrant, about 1 minute. Add tomatoes; cook until heated through, about 5 minutes. Pour balsamic vinegar into tomato mixture; add basil. Cook and stir tomato mixture until flavors blend, about 3 minutes.

3. Place salmon on a plate and top with tomato sauce.

AMAZINGLY EASY TURKEY BREAST

Total Time: 8hr 10 min
Prep: 10 min
Cook: 8hr

6 Servings
2 Nutrient-Dense Protein Per Serving
1 Whole-Food Fat Per Serving

Ingredients

- 5/8 (6 pound) bone-in turkey breast
- 5/8 (1 ounce) envelope dry onion soup mix

Directions

1. Rinse the turkey breast and pat dry.

2. Cut off any excess skin, but leave the skin covering the breast.

3. Rub onion soup mix all over outside of the turkey and under the skin.

4. Place in a slow cooker.

5. Cover, and cook on High for 1 hour, then set to Low, and cook for 7 hours.

Mustard Glazed Savory Salmon

Total Time: 15 min
Prep: 10 min
Cook: 5 min

8 Servings
1 Nutrient-Dense Protein Per Serving
1 Whole-Food Fat Per Serving

Ingredients

- 1 tablespoon and 1 teaspoon extra virgin coconut oil
- 1/4 cup and 2 tablespoons Dijon mustard
- 2 tablespoons and 2 teaspoons rice vinegar
- 2 teaspoons Sriracha hot sauce (optional)
- salt to taste
- 8 (5 ounce) salmon fillets

Directions

1. Set oven rack about 6 inches from the heat source and preheat the oven's broiler. Line a baking sheet with aluminum foil and rub with coconut oil.

2. Stir mustard, vinegar, Sriracha sauce, and salt together in a bowl until glaze is smooth.

3. Lay salmon fillets, skin-side down, on the prepared baking sheet. Brush fillets with mustard glaze.

4. Cook in the preheated oven until salmon is golden and flakes easily with a fork, 5 to 8 minutes.

MINI MEATLOAVES

Total Time: 1hr 25 min
Prep: 20 min
Cook: 1hr 5 min

8 Servings
1 Nutrient-Dense Protein Per Serving
2 Whole-Food Fats Per Serving

Ingredients

- 2-1/2 teaspoons extra virgin coconut oil
- 1/2 cup and 1 tablespoon and 2 teaspoons diced carrots
- 1/2 cup and 1 tablespoon and 2 teaspoons diced onion
- 3/4 (14.5 ounce) can fire-roasted diced tomatoes
- 3/4 cup and 2 teaspoons lightly packed fresh spinach leaves

- 2-1/2 cloves garlic, chopped
- 3/4 large pinch chopped fresh thyme
- 3/4 large pinch chopped fresh parsley
- salt and ground black pepper to taste
- 2-1/4 pounds lean ground beef
- 3/4 egg, lightly beaten
- 2-1/2 slices bacon, cut into 10 pieces

Directions

1. Heat oil in a saucepan over medium heat. Cook and stir carrots and onion in hot oil until slightly softened, 3 to 7 minutes. Add tomatoes, spinach, garlic, thyme, parsley, salt, and black pepper; bring to a simmer, reduce heat to medium-low, and simmer until flavors combine, about 20 minutes. Cool slightly, 5 to 10 minutes.

2. Preheat oven to 400 degrees F (200 degrees C). Line a baking sheet with aluminum foil.

3. Puree vegetable mixture using a stick blender until smooth. Alternatively, pour vegetable mixture into a blender no more than half full. Cover and hold lid down; pulse a few times before leaving on to blend. Puree in batches until smooth.

4. Mix pureed vegetables, ground beef, and egg together in a bowl with your hands until evenly combined. Divide meat mixture into 10 equal portions; form each into a mini-loaf and place on prepared baking sheet. Place 1 bacon piece on top of each loaf.

5. Bake in the preheated oven until no longer pink in the center, 40 to 45 minutes. An instant-read thermometer inserted into the center should read at least 160 degrees F (70 degrees C).

Pork Roast

Total Time: 1hr 15 min
Prep: 15 min
Cook: 1hr

8 Servings
2 Nutrient-Dense Protein Per Serving
2 Whole-Food Fats Per Serving

Ingredients

- 2 tablespoons fresh rosemary
- 2-3/4 teaspoons garlic salt
- 3/4 teaspoon dried thyme
- 1/4 teaspoon freshly ground black pepper
- 4 pounds boneless pork loin roast

Directions

1. Preheat oven to 350 degrees F (175 degrees C).

2. In a large, resealable plastic bag, mix rosemary, garlic salt, thyme, and pepper. Place pork roast in the bag, seal, and toss until thoroughly coated with the garlic salt mixture. Transfer to a medium baking dish.

3. Cook pork roast 1 hour in the preheated oven, or to an internal temperature of 145 degrees F (63 degrees C).

ROAST BEEF

Total Time: 8hr 15 min 8 Servings
Prep: 15 min 2 Nutrient-Dense Protein Per Serving
Cook: 8hr 1 Whole-Food Fat Per Serving

Ingredients

- 3-1/2 pounds rump roast
- 1-1/4 (10.75 ounce) cans condensed cream of mushroom soup
- 1-1/4 (10.5 ounce) cans condensed beef broth

Directions

1. Place rump roast in a slow cooker. Pour in condensed cream of mushroom soup and condensed beef broth. Cook on LOW for about 8 hours.

ROAST SIRLOIN

Total Time: 2hr 45 min   8 Servings
Prep: 30 min   2 Nutrient-Dense Protein Per Serving
Cook: 2hr 15 min   1 Whole-Food Fat Per Serving

Ingredients

- 2 tablespoons extra virgin coconut oil
- 1 (3 pound) beef sirloin tip roast
- 1 onion, chopped
- 4 cloves garlic, minced
- 2 cups brewed coffee
- 1 1/2 cups water

- 2 cubes beef bouillon
- 6 basil leaves
- 1 tablespoon salt
- 1 teaspoon ground black pepper
- 1/2 cup all-purpose flour
- 1/2 cup water
- salt to taste

Directions

1. Heat extra virgin coconut oil in stock pot over medium heat; sear roast in the hot oil until slightly browned, about 2 minutes per side. Remove roast from pot and place on a plate. Cook and stir onion and garlic in the hot oil until onion is lightly browned, 10 to 15 minutes.

2. Return seared roast to the stock pot; pour coffee and 1 1/2 cup water over roast. Add beef bouillon, basil leaves, 1 tablespoon salt, and pepper.

3. Bring broth to a boil; reduce heat to medium low, cover stock pot, and simmer until meat is falling apart, 2 to 3 hours. Remove and discard basil leaves. Transfer roast to a serving dish and cover with a lid or aluminum foil, keeping the broth in the stock pot over medium heat.

4. Whisk flour and 1/2 cup water together in a bowl until smooth. Slowly whisk flour mixture into broth until gravy is smooth and somewhat clear; season with salt. Pour about half the gravy over the roast and pour the rest into a gravy boat for serving.

Robust Flap Steak

Total Time: 15 min
Prep: 10 min
Cook: 5 min

8 Servings
2 Nutrient-Dense Protein Per Serving
2 Whole-Food Fats Per Serving

Ingredients

- 1/4 cup green curry paste
- 1/4 cup fish sauce, or more to taste
- 1/4 cup rice vinegar, or more to taste
- 1/4 cup coconut milk

- freshly ground black pepper to taste
- 2 pinches cayenne pepper, or more to taste
- 2 pinches salt (optional)
- 4 pounds flap steak, trimmed of fat

Directions

1. Whisk curry paste, fish sauce, rice vinegar, coconut milk, black pepper, cayenne pepper, and salt together in a large shallow glass or ceramic bowl. Add the flap steak and turn to evenly coat. Cover the bowl with plastic wrap and marinate in the refrigerator for 4 to 12 hours.

2. Remove the flap meat from the marinade and shake off excess. Discard remaining marinade.

3. Preheat an outdoor grill for high heat and lightly oil the grate.

4. Cook flap steak on the preheated grill until it starts to firm and is reddish-pink and juicy in the center, 2 to 3 minutes per side. An instant-read thermometer inserted into the center should read 130 degrees F (54 degrees C). Transfer meat to a plate to rest for at least five minutes before slicing against the grain.

SALISBURY STEAKS

Total Time: 25 min
Prep: 15 min
Cook: 10 min

8 Servings
1 Nutrient-Dense Protein Per Serving
1 Whole-Food Fat Per Serving

Ingredients

- 2 pounds extra-lean ground beef
- 1/4 cup minced onion
- 1/4 cup minced green bell pepper
- 2 tablespoons finely chopped fresh parsley
- 2 teaspoons salt
- 2 teaspoons paprika
- 2 cloves garlic, minced
- 1/2 teaspoon ground black pepper
- 1/2 pinch dried thyme leaves
- 2 tablespoons almond flour
- 2 tablespoons extra virgin coconut oil, or as needed

Directions

1. Set oven rack about 6 inches from the heat source and preheat the oven's broiler. Line a baking sheet with aluminum foil.

2. Mix ground beef, onion, green bell pepper, parsley, salt, paprika, garlic, black pepper, and thyme together in a bowl; divide into 4 portions and shape into patties. Arrange patties on the prepared baking sheet. Dust both sides of patties with flour and brush with melted oil.

3. Broil in the preheated oven until steaks are cooked through, 4 to 8 minutes per side. An instant-read thermometer inserted into the center should read at least 160 degrees F (70 degrees C).

SANE Ham Steaks

Total Time: 20 min
Prep: 10 min
Cook: 10 min

8 Servings
1 Nutrient-Dense Protein Per Serving
2 Whole-Food Fats Per Serving

Ingredients

- 2 pounds ham steak
- extra virgin coconut oil cooking spray
- ground black pepper to taste
- 1/4 cup and 2 tablespoons extra virgin coconut oil
- 2 tablespoons Dijon mustard

- 2 tablespoons lemon juice
- 2 teaspoons champagne vinegar
- 1/2 teaspoon ground black pepper
- 4 (10 ounce) packages mixed salad greens
- 2/3 cup crumbled reduced-fat feta cheese

Directions

1. Preheat an outdoor grill for medium-high heat and lightly oil the grate.

2. Coat ham steak on both sides with cooking spray; season with black pepper to taste.

3. Grill ham on preheated grill until meat shows good grill marks, 4 to 5 minutes per side. Cut ham into bite-size pieces.

4. Whisk melted coconut oil, Dijon mustard, lemon juice, champagne vinegar, and 1/4 teaspoon black pepper in a large bowl. Toss mixed greens into dressing to coat. Divide salad onto four plates and top with ham and feta cheese.

Savory Crusted Catfish

Total Time: 42 min
Prep: 30 min
Cook: 12 min

8 Servings
2 Nutrient-Dense Protein Per Serving
3 Whole-Food Fats Per Serving

Ingredients

- 2 cups coconut flour
- 1 teaspoon chili powder, or to taste
- 1/2 teaspoon salt
- 1/2 teaspoon black pepper
- 2 egg, beaten
- 2 tablespoons extra virgin coconut oil
- 8 (8 ounce) fillets catfish, washed and patted dry

Directions

1. Preheat oven to 450 degrees F (230 degrees C). Line a cooking sheet with aluminum foil and spray lightly with cooking spray.
2. In a shallow dish, mix together coconut flour, chili powder, salt, and pepper.
3. In another bowl, mix egg and oil. Dip catfish in egg and oil mixture, then dredge in coconut mixture. Place catfish on foil-lined baking sheet, and sprinkle any leftover chip mixture over the catfish.
4. Bake in a preheated oven until catfish is flaky and white in the middle, 10 to 12 minutes.

SEAFOOD GUMBO

Total Time: 1hr 30 min
Prep: 30 min
Cook: 1hr

8 Servings
1 Nutrient-Dense Protein Per Serving
1 Whole-Food Fat Per Serving

Ingredients

- 3 tablespoons and 1/2 teaspoon extra virgin coconut oil
- 3/4 large onion, chopped
- 3/4 bell pepper, chopped
- 1-1/2 stalks celery, chopped
- 1-1/2 cloves garlic, minced
- 3-1/4 cubes beef bouillon
- 4-3/4 cups hot water
- 3/4 (28 ounce) can diced tomatoes, undrained
- 3/4 (16 ounce) package frozen sliced okra
- 3-1/4 cups shrimp, peeled and deveined
- 1-1/2 teaspoons salt
- 1/4 teaspoon cayenne pepper
- 1/2 teaspoon dried thyme
- 1-1/2 bay leaves
- 3/4 teaspoon dry crab boil
- 1-1/2 pounds catfish fillets, cut into 1 inch pieces

Directions

1. Warm oil in a skillet over medium heat. Stir in onion, bell pepper, celery, and garlic. Cook until soft, about 10 minutes.

2. Dissolve bouillon cubes in hot water. Pour into skillet. Stir tomatoes, okra, and shrimp into skillet. Season with salt, cayenne pepper, thyme, bay leaves, and crab boil. Bring to a boil; cover, and simmer 30 minutes.

3. Place fish in skillet, return to boil; cover, and simmer 15 minutes more. Remove bay leaves, and serve.

SIRLOIN TIP ROAST

Total Time: 1hr 45 min   8 Servings
Prep: 5 min   1 Nutrient-Dense Protein Per Serving
Cook: 1hr 40 min   2 Whole-Food Fats Per Serving

Ingredients

- 4 pounds beef sirloin tip roast
- 5-1/4 cloves garlic, peeled and halved
- 1-1/4 teaspoons coarsely ground black pepper

Directions

1. Preheat oven to 400 degrees F (200 degrees C). Secure roast with cooking twine.

2. Make 8 (1/2 inch) slits around the roast, and insert 1/2 garlic clove into each slit. Sprinkle with fresh ground pepper. Place on a rack in roasting pan.

3. Roast in preheated oven for 20 minutes. Reduce heat to 325 degrees F, and insert meat thermometer into roast. Continue cooking about 1 hour, or to desired doneness; remove from oven. Loosely cover with foil, and let roast stand 15 minutes before slicing.

4. To serve, slice thinly against the grain, and use pan drippings for gravy.

SLOW COOKED HERBED TURKEY

Total Time: 6hr 15 min
Prep: 15 min
Cook: 6hr

8 Servings
2 Nutrient-Dense Protein Per Serving
1 Whole-Food Fat Per Serving

Ingredients

- 5/8 (5 pound) boneless turkey breast
- salt and ground black pepper to taste
- 3-1/4 sprigs fresh rosemary, divided
- 3-1/4 sprigs fresh thyme, divided

- 5/8 white onion, chopped – divided
- 1/3 cup butter, sliced into pats
- 1-1/3 cups chopped fresh celery leaves
- 3/8 (750 milliliter) bottle white wine, or more to taste

Directions

1. Rinse turkey breast and pat dry with paper towels; sprinkle with salt and black pepper. Place 2 rosemary sprigs, 2 thyme sprigs, 1/4 cup chopped onion, and butter slices into turkey breast cavity.

2. Place celery leaves, remaining white onion, and remaining rosemary and thyme sprigs into a large slow cooker. Lay turkey breast over vegetables and herbs with the top facing down. Pour white wine into cooker and cover.

3. Cook on High until meat is tender and an instant-read meat thermometer inserted into the thickest part of the breast meat reads 170 degrees (75 degrees C), about 6 hours. Let turkey breast rest for 15 minutes before slicing.

SPEEDY POACHED SALMON

Total Time: 17 min
Prep: 10 min
Cook: 7 min

8 Servings
1 Nutrient-Dense Protein Per Serving
2 Whole-Food Fats Per Serving

Ingredients

- 1/2 cup butter
- 1/2 cup white wine
- 2 tablespoons lemon juice
- 2 tablespoons dried dill weed

- 2 teaspoons white sugar
- salt and ground black pepper to taste
- 8 salmon fillets

Directions

1. Combine butter, wine, lemon juice, dill, sugar, salt, and black pepper together in a microwave-safe casserole dish; place cover on dish.

2. Microwave butter mixture until butter is melted, 45 to 60 seconds. Add salmon, skin-side up, to butter mixture and place cover on dish. Microwave until salmon flakes easily with a fork, about 6 minutes.

TANGY TROUT

Total Time: 20 min
Prep: 12 min
Cook: 8 min

8 Servings
2 Nutrient-Dense Protein Per Serving
2 Whole-Food Fats Per Serving

Ingredients

- 2 cups plain yogurt
- 2 cucumber, shredded
- 1/4 cup chopped fresh dill weed
- 2 teaspoons lemon zest

- 2 tablespoons extra virgin coconut oil
- salt and pepper to taste
- 8 (6 ounce) fillets rainbow trout
- 2 pinches lemon pepper

Directions

1. In a medium bowl combine the yogurt, cucumber, dill, lemon zest, melted extra virgin coconut oil and salt and pepper. Mix well and set aside.

2. Turn oven broiler on. Coat a broiler pan with non-stick cooking spray.

3. Sprinkle fillets with lemon pepper and place on broiler pan. broil for about 8 minutes or until fish flakes with a fork. To serve spoon yogurt sauce over fish.

TEMPTING BAKED TILAPIA

Total Time: 30 min
Prep: 10 min
Cook: 20 min

8 Servings
1 Nutrient-Dense Protein Per Serving
1 Whole-Food Fat Per Serving
1 Most-Dairy Per Serving

Ingredients

- 8 (4 ounce) fillets tilapia
- salt and pepper to taste
- 2 tablespoons Cajun seasoning, or to taste
- 2 lemon, thinly sliced
- 1/2 cup mayonnaise
- 1 cup sour cream
- 1/4 teaspoon garlic powder
- 2 teaspoons fresh lemon juice
- 1/4 cup chopped fresh dill
- extra virgin coconut oil cooking spray

Directions

1. Preheat the oven to 350 degrees F (175 degrees C). Lightly coat a 9×13 inch baking dish with extra virgin coconut oil cooking spray.

2. Season the tilapia fillets with salt, pepper and Cajun seasoning on both sides. Arrange the seasoned fillets in a single layer in the baking dish. Place a layer of lemon slices over the fish fillets. I usually use about 2 slices on each piece so that it covers most of the surface of the fish.

3. Bake uncovered for 15 to 20 minutes in the preheated oven, or until fish flakes easily with a fork.

4. While the fish is baking, mix together the mayonnaise, sour cream, garlic powder, lemon juice and dill in a small bowl. Serve with tilapia.

TURKEY CASSEROLE

Total Time: 2hr 15 min
Prep: 25 min
Cook: 1hr 50 min

8 Servings
2 Nutrient-Dense Protein Per Serving
1 Whole-Food Fat Per Serving

Ingredients

- 1 tablespoon and 1 teaspoon butter
- 1 tablespoon and 1 teaspoon extra virgin coconut oil
- 1-1/4 large onion, sliced
- 5/8 green bell pepper, cut into chunks
- 5/8 red bell pepper, cut into chunks
- 2-1/4 pounds turkey leg meat, cut into 1-inch cubes

- 10-1/2 large whole fresh mushrooms
- 1-1/4 apple, cored and sliced
- 2-3/4 cloves garlic, crushed
- 1-1/3 cups dry white wine
- 1-1/4 sprigs fresh thyme
- 1-1/4 sprigs fresh oregano
- 1-1/4 sprigs fresh parsley
- 1-1/4 sprigs fresh sage
- salt and ground black pepper to taste

Directions

1. Preheat oven to 350 degrees F (175 degrees C).

2. Heat the butter and extra virgin coconut oil in a large skillet, and cook the onion until translucent, stirring occasionally, about 5 minutes.

3. Stir in the green and red peppers, and cook for 5 more minutes, then transfer the vegetables with a slotted spoon into a 2-quart baking dish.

4. Stir the turkey meat into the hot oil left in the skillet, and cook until browned, about 8 to 10 minutes; place the turkey into the baking dish. Mix the mushrooms, apple, and garlic into the turkey and vegetables.

5. Pour the white wine into the dish. With a small piece of kitchen twine, tie the sprigs of thyme, oregano, parsley, and sage into a little bundle, and drop it into the baking dish. Sprinkle with salt and pepper.

6. Cook in the preheated oven until the turkey is tender, 1 1/2 to 2 hours; remove the herb bundle before serving.

ZESTY PORK TENDERLOIN

Total Time: 50 min   8 Servings
Prep: 15 min   1 Nutrient-Dense Protein Per Serving
Cook: 35 min   3 Whole-Food Fats Per Serving

Ingredients

- 1/4 cup extra virgin coconut oil
- 1/2 cup chopped prosciutto
- 1/4 cup chopped fresh sage
- 1/4 cup chopped fresh parsley
- 1/4 cup chopped oil-packed sun-dried tomatoes

- 1/2 cup chopped onion
- 3 pounds pork tenderloin, cut into 1/2 inch strips
- 1 cup chicken broth
- 1 cup heavy cream
- 1/2 teaspoon salt
- 1 teaspoon ground black pepper

Directions

1. Heat the oil in a skillet over medium-high heat. Sauté the prosciutto, sage, parsley, sun-dried tomatoes, and onion 5 minutes, until onion is tender. Mix the pork strips into the skillet, and brown about 10 minutes, turning once.

2. Stir the broth and heavy cream into the skillet, and season with salt and pepper. Bring to a boil. Reduce heat to low, and simmer 20 minutes, stirring occasionally, until pork reaches a minimum temperature of 145 degrees F (63 degrees C) and sauce is thickened.

SOUP

Improve Your Weight Loss, Energy, Mood, and Digestion In Just 17 Second A Day!

 0g Sugar

 100% Plant-Based

 Gluten Free

 No GMO's

 No Dairy

 No Soy

Introducing *Garden In My Glass*. The quickest, easiest, and most affordable way to get your family eating their fruits and veggies...and loving it!

When you order today you will also receive our wildly popular *'28 Days Of Green Smoothies'* recipe collection.

Plus, Get A Green Smoothie Recipe Book for FREE!

LEARN MORE AT: GardenInMyGlass.com

Arugula Soup

Total Time: 25 min
Prep: 10 min
Cook: 15 min

6 Servings
1 Non-Starchy Vegetable Per Serving

Ingredients

- 1 tablespoon extra virgin coconut oil
- 1 medium onion, chopped
- 2 garlic cloves, chopped
- 1 teaspoon cornstarch
- 6 cups low-sodium chicken broth
- 1/2 cup low-fat evaporated milk

- 2 (5-ounce) containers baby arugula
- 1/4 cup mixed chopped herbs (such as mint, chives, parsley, and tarragon)
- 4 tablespoons plain Greek yogurt
- 2 tablespoons sliced chives

Directions

1. Heat extra virgin coconut oil in a large saucepan over medium-low heat.

2. Add onion and garlic; cook until translucent (5 minutes).

3. Stir in cornstarch; whisk in chicken broth and evaporated milk; bring to a simmer.

4. Stir in arugula and mixed chopped herbs until wilted; cover and set aside 5 minutes.

5. Use an immersion blender to blend until smooth.

6. Divide among 6 bowls; garnish each with 2 tsp plain Greek yogurt and 1 tsp sliced chives.

ASIAN VEGETABLE SOUP

Total Time: 10 min
Prep: 5 min
Cook: 5 min

4 Servings
1 Non-Starchy Vegetable Per Serving

Ingredients

- 2 (13 3/4 ounce) cans beef broth
- 1/4 cup dry sherry
- 1/3 cup sliced celery
- 2 scallions, sliced
- 1 tablespoon soy sauce

- 1/4 cup drained sliced water chestnuts
- 4 medium fresh mushrooms, sliced
- 1 (7 ounce) package frozen pea pods
- scallion, curls for garnish

Directions

1. In saucepan, combine first 6 ingredients. Bring to boil. Reduce heat and simmer 3 minutes.

2. Add mushrooms and pea pods. Simmer 2 minutes.

3. Garnish with scallion curl and serve.

CABBAGE SOUP

Total Time: 40 min
Prep: 10 min
Cook: 30 min

2 Servings
1 Non-Starchy Vegetable Per Serving

Ingredients

- 2 cups cabbage, chopped finely in strips
- 5 cups chicken broth

- 2-3 carrots, chopped finely in strips (optional)
- salt and pepper

Directions

1. Cut the cabbage and carrots finely in strips.

2. Heat the chicken broth in a large casserole.

3. Add the cabbage and carrots.

4. Let boil 20 to 25 minutes.

5. You can add seasonning to your own taste.

Cabbage Soup Lithuanian Style

Total Time: 3hr 20 min   8 Servings
Prep: 20 min   1 Non-Starchy Vegetable Per Serving
Cook: 3hr

Ingredients

- 1 lb sauerkraut
- 5 cups chicken stock, low-sodium recommended
- 2 cups water
- 1 1/2 lbs smoked ham hocks

- 5 peppercorns
- 2 whole bay leaves
- 2 medium tomatoes, cored, seeded and diced
- 1 medium onion, chopped
- 1/2 medium head of cabbage, shredded

Directions

1. In a large pot, place the sauerkraut, chicken stock, smoked meat, peppercorns and bay leaves. Add water to cover. Bring to a boil, reduce temperature, cover and simmer for 1 to 2 hours. Meat should be tender.

2. Remove meat, discard bones, dice and return to the pot. Add the shredded cabbage, tomatoes and onion. Bring to a boil, reduce to a simmer and cook another hour or so.

3. Add water, as necessary, to keep it soupy.

4. To serve, remove the bay leaves and dish up, with hot boiled potatoes on the side.

5. Note: If you prefer, substitute 1 cup shredded carrots for the tomatoes. Smoked turkey is a good substitute for the ham hocks. And there is nothing wrong with a nice hambone!

6. Note2: You can drain and rinse the sauerkraut for a milder dish, but I think this is pretty mild, because of all the liquid and the fresh cabbage.

7. Note3: You can reduce the amount of chicken stock if you need to – the meat will add a lot of substance to the liquid. I also have used the strained liquid left over after cooking a corned beef in the crock.

CREAM OF CAULIFLOWER SOUP

Total Time: 1hr 5 min
Prep: 5 min
Cook: 1hr

6 Servings
1 Non-Starchy Vegetable Per Serving

Ingredients

- 1 medium head cauliflower, cut into flowerets
- 2 stalks celery, cut into pieces
- 1 medium onion, chopped
- salt and pepper
- 4-6 cups chicken broth
- 1/2 cup light cream (optional)
- 1/2 teaspoon Worcestershire sauce
- 1/8 teaspoon nutmeg

Directions

1. In a big stock pot add cauliflower, celery, onion, salt and pepper.
2. Cook until tender, about 1 hour.
3. Cool, then put thru a Blender.
4. Pour back into pot, add Worcestershire sauce and nutmeg and cream.
5. Cook until heated thru.
6. Serve with nice bread or rolls.

GINGER CARROT SOUP

Total Time: 40 min
Prep: 15 min
Cook: 25 min

4 Servings
1 Non-Starchy Vegetable Per Serving

Ingredients

- 8 carrots (1 pound), sliced, leaves reserved for garnish
- 1 tablespoon chopped fresh ginger
- 1 large clove garlic, smashed
- 1/4 teaspoon crushed red pepper, plus additional for garnish

- 1/2 teaspoon kosher salt
- 4 cups water
- 2 teaspoons fresh lemon juice

Directions

1. In large pot, simmer carrots and next 5 ingredients (through water), covered, until carrots are tender (20-25 minutes).

2. Using an immersion blender (or a standard, blender working in batches), blend until smooth; add lemon juice. Divide among 4 bowls; garnish with crushed red pepper and carrot leaves. If desired, serve chilled.

GINGER SEAFOOD SOUP

Total Time: 1hr
Prep: 20 min
Cook: 40 min

4 Servings
1 Non-Starchy Vegetable Per Serving

Ingredients

- 1 teaspoon extra virgin coconut oil
- 2 garlic cloves, minced
- 1 tablespoon fresh gingerroot, peeled and minced
- 1 teaspoon lemon peel, grated
- 1/4 teaspoon dried red pepper flakes
- 4 cups low sodium chicken broth
- 1 tablespoon low sodium soy sauce
- 1 tablespoon fresh lemon juice
- 3 carrots, peeled and sliced thinly
- 1/4 lb scallops, diced
- 1/4 lb large shrimp, peeled and diced
- 1 teaspoon sesame oil
- 4 green onions, chopped fine
- 2 tablespoons fresh cilantro, chopped

Directions

1. Heat extra virgin coconut oil in large saucepan or Dutch oven.

2. Add garlic, ginger, lemon peel and hot pepper flakes. Cook gently until very fragrant.

3. Add broth, soy sauce and lemon juice and bring to boil.

4. Add carrots. Reduce heat and simmer gently for 15 minutes.

5. Add scallops, shrimp, sesame oil and green onions, Cook for just a few minutes, or until seafood is barely cooked.

6. Serve sprinkled with cilantro.

.

ITALIAN STYLE EGG DROP SOUP

Total Time: 55 min
Prep: 5 min
Cook: 10 min

4 Servings
1 Non-Starchy Vegetable Per Serving

Ingredients

- 5 cups chicken broth
- 2 large eggs
- 3 tablespoons grated parmesan cheese
- 1/4 cup minced Italian parsley
- salt and pepper

Directions

1. Bring stock to a boil in a large saucepan.

2. Beat together eggs, Parmesan cheese and parsley in a bowl.

3. Reduce heat to low on stock and drizzle egg mixture into stock.

4. Simmer, stirring until eggs are set.

5. Season with salt and pepper.

MISO MUSHROOM SOUP

Total Time: 55 min   1 Serving
Prep: 5 min   1 Non-Starchy Vegetable Per Serving
Cook: 10 min

Ingredients

- 1/2 pint water (with or without a small amount of vegetable stock)
- 2 shiitake mushrooms
- 1 scallion
- 1 tablespoon miso
- 1/2 cup firm tofu, diced

Directions

1. Slice Shiitake mushrooms.

2. Slice up green part of scallion, to garnish later.

3. Bring water (with stock if desired) to boil.

4. Stir in miso paste and mushrooms.

5. Lower heat, simmer for 5 minutes.

6. Pour into serving dish, add tofu, sprinkle scallion on.

7. Serve immediately.

QUICK EGG DROP SOUP

Total Time: 22 min
Prep: 10 min
Cook: 12 min

4 Servings
1 Whole-Food Fat Per Serving

Ingredients

- 6 cups chicken broth
- 1/2 tablespoon grated fresh ginger or 1 teaspoon powdered ginger
- 3 eggs, beaten
- 1 tablespoon scallion, finely sliced

Directions

1. Bring broth and ginger to a boil.

2. Whisk in beaten eggs. Cook for 1-2 more minutes.

3. Add scallions, stir.

4. Serve steaming hot.

5. You could add soy sauce to taste at the table.

6. You could add finely sliced celery and grated carrots just before the eggs. That way you get some veggies inches Good idea with picky children.

SIMPLE CREAM OF MUSHROOM SOUP

Total Time: 15 min
Prep: 5 min
Cook: 10 min

2 Servings
1 Non-Starchy Vegetable Per Serving

Ingredients

- 1 cup chopped mushroom
- 2 tablespoons light sour cream

- 1/4 cup water
- 2 (3/4 ounce) wedges Laughing Cow cheese

Directions

1. Sauté mushrooms till soft

2. Add remaining ingredients and heat through until cheese is melted.

3. Makes two servings at 1 point.

SPINACH SOUP ROMAN STYLE

Total Time: 20 min
Prep: 10 min
Cook: 10 min

8 Servings
1 Non-Starchy Vegetable Per Serving
1 Whole-Food Fat Per Serving

Ingredients

- 6 cups reduced-sodium chicken broth
- 1 cup egg whites
- 1/4 cup minced fresh basil
- 3 tablespoons freshly grated parmesan cheese
- 2 tablespoons lemon juice
- 1 tablespoon minced fresh parsley

- 1/4 teaspoon white pepper
- 1/8 teaspoon ground nutmeg
- 8 cups fresh spinach, washed, stems removed, and coarsley chopped
- lemon slice (to garnish)
- parsley sprig (to garnish)
- 4 cups cooked chicken diced

Directions

1. In a 4-qt saucepan, over medium heat, bring broth to a boil.
2. Beat together eggs, basil, cheese, lemon juice, parsley, white pepper and nutmeg.
3. Set aside.
4. Add spinach and chicken to broth and simmer 1 minute.
5. Slowly pour egg mixture into broth while whisking constantly so that egg threads form.
6. Simmer 2 to 3 minutes or until egg is cooked.
7. Garnish with lemon slices and parsley.
8. Note: Soup may look curdled.

Zucchini Curry Soup

Total Time: 40 min
Prep: 10 min
Cook: 30 min

6 Servings
1 Non-Starchy Vegetable Per Serving

Ingredients

- 2 tablespoons extra virgin coconut oil
- 1 medium onion, chopped
- 1 clove garlic, minced
- 2 teaspoons curry powder
- 2 pounds zucchini (about 6), trimmed, coarsely chopped
- 4 cups low-sodium chicken or vegetable broth
- Salt and freshly ground black pepper
- 1 cup reduced-fat sour cream
- 2 tablespoons chopped fresh cilantro for garnish

Directions

1. Warm oil in a pot over medium heat. Add onion and sauté until softened, 6 to 8 minutes. Add garlic and curry powder and stir until fragrant, about 1 minute. Raise heat to medium-high, add zucchini, pour in broth and add 1 tsp. salt. Cover and bring to a simmer. Remove cover, reduce heat to medium to maintain a simmer and cook until zucchini is very tender, about 20 minutes. Remove from heat and let soup cool slightly.

2. Working in batches, puree soup in a blender until smooth. Transfer to a large bowl, cover and refrigerate until chilled, at least 2 hours.

3. Just before serving, whisk in sour cream and season with salt and pepper. Ladle into chilled bowls, garnish with cilantro and serve

Zucchini Soup

Total Time: 25 min
Prep: 10 min
Cook: 15 min

4 Servings
1 Non-Starchy Vegetable Per Serving

Ingredients

- 3 cups chicken broth
- 1 1/2 lbs zucchini, cut into 1-inch pieces (about 3 medium)
- 1 tablespoon chopped fresh tarragon or 1 tablespoon dill or 1 teaspoon dried dill
- 3/4 cup shredded cheddar cheese (3 oz)
- 1/4 teaspoon salt
- 1/4 teaspoon fresh ground black pepper

Directions

1. Place broth, zucchini and tarragon (or dill) in a medium saucepan; bring to a boil over high heat. Reduce to a simmer and cook, uncovered, until the zucchini is tender, 7-10 minutes.

2. Puree in a blender, in batches if necessary, until smooth. Return the soup to the pan and heat over medium-high heat, slowly stirring in cheese until it is incorporated. Remove from heat and season with salt and pepper. Serve hot or chilled.

So Much To Look Forward To...

You will learn much more about this as we start your personal weight-loss plan together in your free half-day Masterclass (reserve your seat at SANESeminar.com), but here are a few key reminders as you're getting started on your SANE journey.

SANE eating is a lifelong, enjoyable, sustainable, simple, and delicious way of eating. **It is not a repackaging of the unsustainable calorie counting diets that failed you.**

I know you understand this already—otherwise you wouldn't be here—but please keep in mind that since SANE isn't a calorie counting diet, you will not suffer through the same calorie counting tools and resources that failed you in the past. For example, **memorizing endless food lists and following unrealistic minute-by-minute meal plans aren't just a pain— they cannot work in the real world**, and they cannot work long term.

Life is crazy. Things happen. And heck, people have different tastes in food, so while minute-by-minute "eat exactly this right now no matter what" endless lists might make for good reality TV, if they worked in the real world, you would have already met your goals. **To get a different result (long-term fat loss and robust health), you MUST take a different approach.** That's what you will find here.

If you approach your new SANE life calmly, gradually, and with the next 30 years in mind rather than the next 30 days, **you will learn the underlying principles that enable you to make the SANE choices easily—forever**.

Think of your new approach as the difference between memorizing the sum of every possible combination of numbers versus learning the underlying principles of how addition works. Once you understand addition, lists and memorization aren't necessary as you know what to do with any combination of numbers—forever.

The same thing applies with food. Once you understand the new science of SANE eating, **you will know exactly what to eat (and what to avoid) everywhere you go—forever—without any lists** or any memorization.

This new approach changes everything and will forever free you from all the confusing and conflicting weight-loss information you've been told. So please allow me to congratulate you on coming to the life-changing realization that **to get different results than you've gotten in the past, you must take a different approach than you used in the past!**

The great news is that when you combine a calm, gradual, long-term, and progress vs. perfection mindset with your scientifically proven SANE tools, program, and coaching, you are **guaranteed to burn belly fat, boost energy, and enjoy an unstoppable sense of self-confidence!**

Your new SANE lifestyle has helped over 100,000 people in over 37 countries burn fat and boost health *long-term*....and it will do the same for you if you let it and trust it.

Thank you for taking the road less travelled...it will make all the difference!

SANEly and Gratefully,

Jonathan Bailor | SANE Founder, NYTimes Bestselling Author, and soon...your personal weight-loss coach

P.S. Over the years I have found that our most successful members, the ones who have lost 60, 70, even 100 pounds... and kept it off... are the ones who start their personal weight-loss plan on...

our **FREE half-day Masterclass**. It's your best opportunity to fall in love with the SANE lifestyle, learn exactly how to start making the simple changes that lead to dramatic body transformations, and get introduced to your new SANE family. Be sure to reserve your spot at http://SANESeminar.com.

Please Don't Lose Your Seat at the FREE Masterclass Seminar!

Reserve your spot now so we can start your perfect personalized weight-loss plan. Space is limited and fills-up quickly. Reserve your spot now so you don't miss out!

Yes! I want to reserve my spot now at SANESeminar.com

About the Author: Jonathan Bailor is a New York Times bestselling author and internationally recognized natural weight loss expert who specializes in using modern science and technology to simplify health. Bailor has collaborated with top scientists for more than 10 years to analyze and apply over 1,300 studies. His work has been endorsed by top doctors and scientists from Harvard Medical School, Johns' Hopkins, The Mayo Clinic, The Cleveland Clinic, and UCLA.

Bailor is the founder of SANESolution.com and serves as the CEO for the wellness technology company Yopti®. He authored the New York Times and USA Today bestselling book *The Calorie Myth*, hosts a popular syndicated health radio show *The SANE Show*, and blogs on *The Huffington Post*. Additionally, Bailor has registered over 25 patents, spoken at Fortune 100 companies and TED conferences for over a decade, and served as a Senior Program Manager at Microsoft where he helped create Nike+ Kinect Training and XBox Fitness.

Get Everything You Need To Burn Fat and Prepare Delicious Meals at the SANE Store

Fat-Burning
Flour

Mood-Boosting
Chocolate Powder

Clean Pea
Protein

Craving Killer
Bake-N-Crisps

Slimming Sugar
Substitute

Clean Whey
Protein

Vanilla Almond
Meal Bars

Craving Killer
Chocolate Truffle

No Added Sugar

100% Natural

Gluten Free

No GMO's

No Dairy

No Soy

SANE™

Find all of these EXCLUSIVE tools, plus over 100 other fat-burning SANE products to help you and your family look and feel your best!

Visit Today: Store.SANESolution.com

Made in the USA
Lexington, KY
12 June 2016